THE PLOWMAN FROM BOHEMIA

THE
PLOWMAN
FROM BOHEMIA

Johannes von Saaz

In the original Early New High German
and in English

Translated by
ALEXANDER and ELIZABETH HENDERSON

Introduction by Reinhold Schneider

FREDERICK UNGAR PUBLISHING CO.
NEW YORK

The introductory essay by Reinhold Schneider
is included by arrangement with Insel Verlag,
and translated by Alexander and Elizabeth Henderson.

*The illustrations in this volume
are reproductions of medieval woodcuts.*

Printed in the United States of America

Library of Congress Catalog Card No. 66-16315

INTRODUCTION

Johannes von Saaz's disputation has stood the test of centuries as a book that brings solace and consolation to its readers. After the latest catastrophe, it even became a bond among those who suffered the terrible, bewildering fate of being driven from their native land (which was also our author's) and scattered far and wide in foreign countries. They formed a community in the Plowman's name. It is true, no doubt, that the reason why the Saaz notary and schoolmaster called himself a plowman is to be found in the humanist tradition which stretches back to antiquity. But in his particular case we may believe that what was involved was not merely scholarly usage which, as Ernst Robert Curtius has said, equated "writing" and "plowing," but also an expression of the author's attitude to the written word and of his estimate of his work. For him his pen was his plow, and his paper was his field. He took his work as seriously as the peasant does his. He delved deeply into the earth, into the hard reality of experience, to bring the truth to light. And thus he found a new way of writing. This was perhaps the first time, after the triumphs of Middle High German poetry, that the language, now in its

Early New High German form, achieved such richness and plastic power, such a wealth of convincing imagery, such closeness to reality along with such innocence, such stark suffering and scorn, such force and flexibility, such alertness to acute contrasts. And similarly the firm, rhythmic conception, both intellectual and artistic, is not easy to match. It is as though the plowman were plowing up virgin soil. Content and form are one; a light plays over every furrow that the plowman draws. In this disputation with death there is a promise that was redeemed only a hundred and twenty years later, with far-reaching effect, by Martin Luther. And it comes as a benediction that this first great poetic work in New High German was born of the deepest suffering, of the courage to push every question to its limit, of profound religious experience. Not a word is wasted. If our language is to be cured of the plague of abstractionism which has threatened it for centuries, then let us go back to the plowed field of Saaz, and we will find the greatest aid in hard work on that field.

Here, then, was a great poet with a great message, a precursor who was a master already. And yet we have only this one work, preserved in doubtful texts, together with a few records and letters which Dr. Willy Krogmann has made known after much research. Finally, there is a portrait of the plowman, in an Office of St. Jerome which he donated to the church of St. Nicholas at Eger. He is shown at the feet of the saint and the mighty lion, a slight pale man dressed in black, almost timidly holding up the book.

There is little doubt that it was at his first wife's death bed that he first experienced the power of Death and began to remonstrate with him. Johannes von Saaz's greatness as a man, which was to make him our contemporary, is that he does not suppress his pain and try to still it with cheap comfort. He leaps into his wife's grave like Hamlet into Ophelia's, and curses the one who took her from him. He

is a deeply pious man, and yet in his search for the form, the sense and the office of Death, he tears veil after veil from the contradictions of creation and step by step penetrates to the terrible paradox that there must be destruction if there is to be life, an end if there is to be a beginning, sorrow where there is love, and that sorrow and love, life and death continually intensify each other. For, as Death says, everyone who is born is at once old enough to die. Death's figure, Death's title are renewed with every birth. So the plowman calls on all creatures to rebel against the necessity without which they could not be. His pain is irrational, for he rages against the law which alone made his happiness possible. At this point there is no way to help him. As Death mockingly says, his lament is nothing but the braying of a jackass. Yet it is at the same time the truth of a deeply stricken heart, it is the truth of God's intended order upon earth, of love and marriage and hearth and home.

It is Johannes von Saaz's greatness as a man that he did not weaken at this point, that he looked Death in the face; and this is the foundation of his poem. It is the greatness of a human figure that is in no way diminished by his human weakness, by the futility of his lamentation, by repeated outbursts of anger, by what seems to be his lack of understanding and his unteachableness. For only through his weakness can man become great.

This greatness, contradictory and thereby convincing, is opposed by the greatness of Death. Who else but St. Francis has thus seen this greatness of Death, in some degree like that of an angel? Profoundly impressive is the way the two opponents face each other—a man in his furious rage, and ordained necessity. With his "Listen! Just listen!" Death of a human figure that is in no way diminished by his knowledge that life is an agony, that healing comes at last, that even the most violent sorrow passes, in his knowledge

of the worth and worthlessness of all things, and of the true value of creation. He is contemptuous of all excess and icy in his scorn of human presumption: "When God called on you to speak . . . When you bore the standard of Alexander . . ." He honors the woman and assures her of honor by summoning her in the beauty of her virtue, as is his unchallengeable right. For the earth is his as heaven is God's and the abyss is Satan's in his time.

Very moving is the drama within the plowman himself. It is expressed in the way he forces himself to acknowledge the majesty of Death by addressing him as "Sir"; in the way he later again flies into a fury and cries for revenge, demands compensation—which incidentally casts doubt on the uniqueness of the lost wife—and in the way he at last becomes ready to listen, to be taught by a higher wisdom and instance. For, "an angry man cannot deal fairly with his neighbor." And it is expressed in the way Death—who is both something and nothing, a power, though not an absolute one, in the temporal world—in a sense becomes the plowman's friend, his stay and counsellor. It appears again in the way it dawns upon the plaintiff that it is not evil he faces, but the embodiment of universal law. Even the utmost suffering is not the final reality. On this earth man can be deprived of nothing whose loss is irreparable, because everything on earth is subject to the law of death and without it could not exist. But even Death himself is a creature. Here on earth patience is befitting, acceptance and measure; absolute happiness is an impossibility; even marriage, however highly praised, can be a hell, the wife without nobility, "ill when there's work, well when there's pleasure." And the night side of life, that stands over against the day side, proves true all that may be said of the vanity of passionately lamented happiness, of the frailty and baseness of the flesh. St. Bridget of Sweden had well understood why God took on a human body, that "bag of

worms" or "bag of filth." Reality is both noble and wretched, is Abelard's yes and no. But these contrasts are not the ultimate truth.

Beyond the greatness of man, suffering, erring, accepting, is the greatness of Death, who at the last becomes a helpful teacher counselling peace, reconciliation with the terrible yet not absolute fact of this world, a clear conscience, possessing as if not possessing; and from the greatness of man through the greatness of Death the poem rises to the ultimate greatness which conquers even Death. This is God, in whom, like the cycle of the seasons in the year, all conflicting forces merge. All things serve Him; every kind of power is held by lease, is a part of the creation that is built of opposites and of conflicting forces. But man, with his passion and his pain, was right to lodge his desperate complaint and pleaded his cause well, as too did Death. Man with his rebellious heart, and Death with his impartial severity, have to be as they are. Their conflict cannot be resolved at their level. But there is a higher power above them. So the plaintiff is awarded honor and Death victory. Without that victory the world could not exist.

The poem's greatness is its conception of man's greatness, of Death's, and of God's, that comprehends all. God is present throughout the whole conflict between man and Death, is in the mind of each. In the year when Johannes von Saaz probably wrote his poem (1401), there was born the fisherman's son Nicholas Krebs, at Cusa, on the Moselle. Following Thomas Aquinas, he proclaimed the divine majesty which brings all contradictions together into simplicity. Going further back we find the Franciscan poet Jacopone da Todi, who died in 1306. A lawyer, a rich, cynical man of the world, he became a stricken man when Death suddenly, during a ball, laid his hand upon the shoulder of his high-born, beautiful wife. He opened her ball dress and

5

found under it a hair shirt—the gown of honor. Like Johannes von Saaz he found at the bier of his beloved the way to God, and looked upon the face in whose sight it is meaningless to distinguish between pleasure and pain, or to weigh one against the other. In the train of St. Francis, the singer of the sun and of death, he proclaimed the depths of love which had opened before him at the body of his beloved wife:

> The sea is without bounds,
> You plunge and fall and drown,
> You watch the shore retreat,
> Are swallowed by the deep.

The great Italian poetry of the thirteenth century, that of Dante, Petrarch, Jacopone, is a lament for the dead which continually rises to ever higher realms.

After the death of his wife on 1 August 1400 Johannes von Saaz did not enter a religious order; he silenced his heart and remained in the secular world. He administered his estates at Saaz, collected the dues granted to him from the meat market, looked after his children, married again, moved to Prague and was a city notary there until his death in 1414. He had come to recognize that man can hold a lease only, not any possession, that happiness is not the ultimate value, that Death is God's sanctified servant who leads man before the face of the incomprehensible. "All things have been reversed," says Death at the end. But the eternal order of things is coming to pass within the city notary: man is right, and so too is Death, because God maintains justice for both.

The last word is a prayer to the incomprehensible, to the "ancient of youthful days," the dark light, the founder of heaven and hell, the seasons of the year which consume each other and yet collaborate in the world's thriving. We suffer from limitation. Sorrow is extinguished in the sight

of God. Death was His messenger. Man came out of the dispute wiser and humbler. There remain to him the prayer for the dead and the care of his field and his vineyard, leased to him as are his native land and his life. There remains to him acceptance of the world, of the mortality of creation, of man in his nobility and his misery. His rights are those of a guest, are half rights. He plows a field which is not his. Before day and night he says Amen.

REINHOLD SCHNEIDER

THE PLOWMAN FROM BOHEMIA

DER ACKERMAN

Das erste capitel

Grimmiger tilger aller lande, schedlicher echter aller werlte, freissamer mörder aller guten leute, ir Tod, euch sei verfluchet! Got, eur tirmer, hasse euch, unselden merung wone bei euch, ungelück hause gewaltiglich zu euch; zumale geschant seit immer! Angst, not und jamer verlassen euch nicht, wo ir wandert; leid, betrübnüß und kummer beleiten euch allenthalben; leidige anfechtung, schendliche zuversicht und schemliche anferung die betwingen euch gröblich an aller stat! Himel, erde, sunne, mone, gestirne, mer, wag, berg, gefilde, tal, aue, der helle abgrund, auch alles, das leben und wesen hat, sei euch unhold, ungünstig und fluchend ewiglichen! In bosheit versinket, in jamerigem ellende verswindet und in der unwiderbringenden swersten achte Gotes, aller leute und jeglicher schepfung alle zukünftige zeit beleibet! Unverschamter bösewicht,

THE PLOWMAN

Chapter One

Curses be upon you, Death, you dire destroyer of all peoples, you evil bandit to all mankind, you, the dreadful murderer of all good folk. May God, your creator, hate you, may a waxing ill dwell with you and woe be upon you with all its might, may you be utterly disgraced for evermore. May dread, need and desolation never leave you wheresoever you go; may sorrow, grief, and affliction attend you in all your ways; may you be fiercely assailed in each and every place by grievous charges, the expectation of shame and the punishments of dishonor! May heaven and earth, the sun, moon, stars, the seas and waters, every mountain and valley, every dale and meadow, may the very depths of hell itself, may all that lives and breathes turn from you, abominate you and curse you to all eternity! Go down in wickedness, vanish in wretched exile, and for all times

eur böse gedechtnüß lebe und taure hin one ende; graue und forchte scheiden von euch nicht, wo ir wandert und wonet. Von mir und aller menniglich sei stetiglichen über euch ernstlich zeter geschriren mit gewundenen henden!

DER TOD

Das ander capitel

Höret, höret, höret neue wunder! Grausame und ungehorte teidinge fechten uns an. Von wann die komen, das ist uns zumale fremde. Doch droens, fluchens, zetergeschreies, hendewindens und allerlei ankrotung sein wir an allen enden unz her wol genesen. Dannoch, sun, wer du bist, melde dich und lautmere, was dir leides von uns widerfaren sei, darumb du uns so unzimlichen handelst, des wir vormals ungewonet sein, allein wir doch manigen künstereichen, edeln, schönen, mechtigen und heftigen leuten ferre über den rein haben gegraset, davon witwen und weisen, landen und leuten leides genügelich ist geschehen. Du tust dem gleiche, als dir ernst sei und dich not swerlich betwinge. Dein klage ist one reime; davon wir prüfen, du wellest durch dönens und reimens willen deinem sin nicht ent-

to come lie under the harshest irrevocable ban of God and man and of all living creatures! O shameless villain, may your evil memory live and endure without end; may horror and fear not depart from you, wherever you go and wherever you dwell. We will wring our hands, I and all mankind, and solemnly raise an everlasting hue and cry against you.

DEATH

Chapter Two

Listen to these new marvels, just listen! Unheard-of, dreadful charges are brought against us. Their source is quite unknown to us. However, we have hitherto everywhere emerged unscathed from all threats, curses, hue and cry, wringing of hands and divers other attacks. Yet say who you are, son, and say what mischief you have suffered from us, that you should treat us in so unseemly a fashion. We have not been accustomed to this heretofore, although we have largely trespassed upon the fields of many a learned, noble, handsome, mighty and important person, whereby great grief has come to widows and orphans, lands and peoples. You act as though you were in earnest, as though sore need pressed hard upon you. Your complaint is not in rhyme, from which we deduce that you do not

weichen. Bistu aber tobend, wütend, twalmig oder anderswie one sinne, so verzeuch, enthalt und bis nicht zu snelle, so swerlich zu fluchen, den worten das du nicht bekümmert werdest mit afterreue. Wene nicht, das du unser herliche und gewaltige macht immer mügest geswechen. Dannoch nenne dich und versweig nicht, welcherlei sachen dir sei von uns so twenglicher gewalt begegent. Rechtfertig wir wol werden, rechtfertig ist unser geferte. Wir wissen nicht, wes du uns so frevellichen zeihest.

DER ACKERMAN

Das III. capitel

Ich bins genant ein ackerman, von vogelwat ist mein pflug, und wone in Behemer lande. Erhessig, widerwertig und widerstrebend sol ich euch immer wesen, wan ir habt mir den zwelften buchstaben, meiner freuden hort, aus dem alphabet gar freissamlich enzücket. Ir habt meiner wünnen lichte sumerblumen mir aus meines herzen anger jemerlichen ausgereutet; ir habt mir meiner selden haft, mein auserwelte turkeltauben arglistiglichen entfremdet; ir habt unwiderbringlichen raub an mir getan! Weget es selber, ob ich icht billich zürne, wüte und klage:

14

mean to sacrifice your sense for the sake of metre and rhyme. But if you are in a fury, a rage, a trance, or otherwise out of your senses, then wait, hold back, do not be overhasty in wild cursing, lest you be afterward cast down by remorse. Do not suppose that you could ever diminish our glorious and mighty power. But give your name, and do not suppress the things in which we have done you such dreadful violence. We shall certainly vindicate ourselves, for we are righteous in all our doings. We do not know what it is of which you so insolently accuse us.

THE PLOWMAN

Chapter Three

I am called a plowman. My plow is the pen, and I live in Bohemia. I shall always hate you, abhor you and resist you, for you have most cruelly ripped out the twelfth letter of my alphabet, the treasure house of my joys. You have sadly uprooted from my heart's meadow the bright summer flower of my delight; you have craftily lured away the stay of my happiness, my chosen turtle dove; you have committed a robbery against me which can never be made good. Bethink yourself whether I have not just grounds for my anger, rage and complaint. It is through you

15

von euch bin ich freudenreiches wesens beraubet, tegelicher guter lebetage enterbet und aller wünnebringender rente geeußert. Frut und fro was ich vormals zu aller stund; kurz und lustsam was mir alle weile tag und nacht, in gleicher maße freudenreich, geudenreich sie beide; ein jegliches jar was mir ein genadenreiches jar. Nu wirt zu mir gesprochen: schab ab! Bei trübem getranke, auf dürrem aste, betrübet, sware und zeherend beleibe ich und heule one underlaß! Also treibet mich der wind, ich swimme dahin durch des wilden meres flut, die tunnen haben überhand genomen, mein anker haftet ninder. Hierumb ich one ende schreien wil: Ir Tod, euch sei verfluchet!

DER TOD

Das IIII. capitel

Wunder nimt uns solcher ungehorter anfechtung, die uns nimmer hat begegent. Bistu es ein ackerman, wonend in Behemer lande, so dünket uns, du tust uns heftiglichen unrecht; wan wir in langer zeit zu Beheim nicht endeliches haben geschaffet, sunder nu neulich in einer festen hübschen stat, auf einem berge werlich gelegen, der haben vier buchstaben, der achzehende, der erste, der dritte und der drei und zwenzigste in dem alphabet, einen namen

that I am bereft of joyful existence, that, day in day out, I am dispossessed of the good life and despoiled of all the revenues of bliss. Once I was glad and gay at all times; day and night were fleet and pleasing, rich in joy and rich in gladness. For me every year was a year of grace. Now the command is: have done! I am left on a withered branch, I drink the turbid water of sorrow and despair, and I weep and lament without cease. Thus the wind drives me; I am adrift in wild seas, their waves overwhelm me; nowhere does my anchor hold. Therefore I will cry without end: Death, be accursed!

DEATH

Chapter Four

We are amazed at such an unheard-of attack, the like of which we have never encountered before. If you are a plowman living in Bohemia, it seems to us that you are doing us a grave injustice, for it is a long while since we did anything of importance in Bohemia, other than just recently in a fine, fortified town, a stronghold on a height. Its name is plaited with four letters, the eighteenth, the first, the third and the twenty-fifth of the alphabet. There we con-

geflochten. Da haben wir mit einer erberen seligen tochter unser genade gewürket; ir buchstabe was der zwelfte. Sie was ganz frum und wandelsfrei; wir mügen wol sprechen wandelsfrei, wan wir waren gegenwürtig, do sie geboren ward. Do sante ir frau Ere einen erenmantel und einen erenkranz; die brachte ir frau Selde. Unzerissen und ungemeiligt den mantel, den erenkranz brachte sie ganz mit ir unz in die gruben. Unser und ir gezeuge ist der erkenner aller herzen. Guter gewissen, freundhold, getreu, gewere und zumale gütig was sie gen allen leuten. Werlich, so stete und so geheure kam uns zu handen selten. Es sei dann die selbe, die du meinest: anders wissen wir keine.

DER ACKERMAN

Das V. capitel

Ja, herre, ich was ir friedel, sie mein amei. Ir habt sie hin, mein durchlustige eugelweide; sie ist dahin, mein frideschilt vür ungemach; enweg ist mein warsagende wünschelrute. Hin ist hin! Da ste ich armer ackerman allein; verswunden ist mein lichter leitestern an dem himel; zu reste ist gegangen meines heiles sunne, auf get sie mir nimmermer! Nicht mer get auf men fluternder morgenstern, gelegen ist sein schein; kein leidvertreib han ich mer, die finster

18

ferred our grace upon an honest and happy daughter; her letter was the twelfth. She was all virtue, without spot. We can well say without spot, for we were present at her birth. Mistress Honor sent her then a gown of honor and a crown of honor, and they were brought to her by Mistress Fortune. The gown she took untorn and unspotted with her to the grave, the crown intact. Our witness and hers is He Who knows all hearts. She had a clear conscience; she was gracious, loyal and true and especially kind to all. So righteous, so excellent a woman has, in truth, seldom come our way. Unless she be the one you mean, we know of none.

THE PLOWMAN

Chapter Five

Yes, sir, I was her lover, she my lass. You have taken her, the dear delight of my eyes; she is gone, my sure shield against adversity, my true divining rod. She is dead and gone, and I, poor plowman, stand here alone. My bright lodestar has vanished from the sky; the sun of my salvation has set and nevermore will rise for me. My radiant morning star will never rise again, its light is put out. Nothing is left to me to banish sorrow; the darkness of night is be-

nacht ist allenthalben vor meinen augen. Ich wene nicht, das icht sei, das mir rechte freude immermer müge widerbringen; wan meiner freuden achtber banier ist mir leider undergangen. Zeter! waffen! von herzen grunde sei immermer geschriren über den verworfen tag und über die leidigen stunde, darin mein herter, steter diamant ist zerbrochen, darin mein rechte fürender leitestab unbarmherziglich mir aus den henden ward gerücket, darin zu meines heiles verneuendem jungbrunnen mir der weg ist verhauen. Ach one ende, we one underlaß immermer! Versinken, gefelle und ewiger fal sei euch, Tod, zu erbeigen gegeben! Lastermeiliger schandung wirdelos und grisgramig ersterbet und in der helle erstinket! Got beraube euch eurer macht und lasse euch zu pulver zerstieben! One zil habet ein teufelisch wesen!

DER TOD

Das VI. capitel

Ein fuchs slug einen slafenden lewen an den backen, darumb ward im sein balg zerissen; ein hase zwackte einen wolf, noch heute ist er zagellos darumb; ein katze krelte einen hund, der da slafen wolte, immer muß sie des hundes feindschaft tragen. Also wiltu dich an uns reiben. Doch glauben

fore my eyes for ever. I do not believe that there is anything which can ever truly bring me joy again, for the proud banner of my joy, alas, is dipped. May the hue and cry issue from the depths of my heart forever, and vengeance be called down for that evil day, that bitter hour, when my hard, strong diamond was smashed, when my pilgrim's staff that led me aright was mercilessly wrenched from my hands, when my way was barred to the quickening fountain of youth that brought salvation. Unending sighs, unintermitted woe, for ever and ever! May your portion, Death, your inheritance, be downfall, destruction and eternal ruin! In ignominious shame die without dignity, gnashing your teeth, and rot in Hell! May God wrest your power from you and may you be ground to dust! May you have a devil's existence without end.

DEATH

Chapter Six

Once a fox struck a sleeping lion in the face, and so his pelt was torn. Once a hare tweaked a wolf, and so he goes tailless to this day. Once a cat scratched a dog that wanted to sleep and ever after she had to bear the dog's enmity. Just so do you seek a quarrel with us. But we think that a servant is al-

wir, knecht knecht, herre beleibe herre. Wir wellen beweisen, das wir rechte wegen, rechte richten und rechte faren in der werlte, niemandes adels schonen, großer kunst nicht achten, keinerlei schöne ansehen, gabe, liebes, leides, alters, jugend und allerlei sachen nicht wegen. Wir tun als die sunne, die scheinet über gute und böse: wir nemen gute und böse in unsern gewalt. Alle die meister, die die geiste künnen twingen, müssen uns ire geiste antwürten und aufgeben; die bilwisse und die zaubrerinne künnen vor uns nicht beleiben, sie hilfet nicht, das sie reiten auf den krücken, das sie reiten auf den böcken. Die erzte, die den leuten das leben lengen, müssen uns zu teile werden, würze, kraut, salben und allerlei apotekenpulverei künnen sie nicht gehelfen. O solten wir allen den feifaltern und heuschrecken rechnung tun umb ir geslechte, an der rechnung würden wir nicht genügen. O solten wir durch aufsatzes, alafanzes, liebes oder leides willen die leute lassen leben, aller der werlte keisertum were nu unser, alle künige hetten ir krone auf unser haubet gesetzet, ir zepter in unser hand geantwurt, des babstes stul mit seiner dreikronter infel weren wir nu gewaltig. Laß sten dein fluchen, sage nicht von Poppenfels neue mere! Haue nicht über dich, so reren dir die spene nicht in die augen!

ways a servant and a lord always a lord. We mean
to prove that we appraise rightly, judge rightly and
proceed rightly in the world, that we spare no one's
noble birth, disregard great ability, pay no heed to
beauty, nor weigh in the balance anyone's gifts,
love, sorrow, age, youth or any other thing. We do
as the sun does which shines upon the good and the
wicked. The good and the wicked we take into our
power. All adepts who can command the spirits
must consign and surrender their spirits to us; goblins and witches cannot withstand us; it is of no
avail to them that they bestride broomsticks, that
they ride on goats. The very physicians who prolong
people's lives must fall to us; no root, herb, salve or
other apothecary's stuff can help them. Were we to
render account of their generations to every butter-
fly and grasshopper, we would never be done with
the accounting. Were we to let people live because
of tribute, gifts, love or sorrow, then the throne of
the world's emperor would now be ours; all kings
would have placed their crowns upon our head and
pressed their scepters into our hands; the Pope's
throne with the triple tiara would now be in our
power. Stop cursing, let's have no new tales of
Braggermount! Don't chop above your head, and
the chips won't fall into your eyes!

DER ACKERMAN

Das VII. capitel

Künde ich euch gefluchen, künde ich euch geschelten, künde ich euch verpfeien, das euch wirs dann übel geschehe, das hettet ir snödlichen wol an mir verdienet. Wan nach großem leide große klage sol folgen; unmenschlich tet ich, wo ich solch löbeliche Gotes gabe, die niemand dann Got allein geben mag, nicht beweinte. Zware trauren sol ich immer; entflogen ist mir mein erenreicher falke. Mein tugendhafte frauen billichen klage ich, wan sie was edel der geburte, reich der eren, schöne, frut über alle ire gespilen, gewachsener persone, warhaftig und züchtig der worte, keusche des leibes, guter und frölicher mitwonung. Ich sweige als mer, ich bin zu swach, alle ir ere und tugend, die Got selber ir hat mitgeteilt, zu volsagen; herre Tod, ir wisset es selber. Umb solch groß herzeleid sol ich euch mit rechte zusachen. Werlich, were icht gutes an euch, es solte euch selber erbarmen. Ich wil keren von euch, von euch nicht gutes sagen, mit allem meinem vermügen wil ich euch ewiglich widerstreben; alle Gotes tirmung sol mir beistendig wesen, wider euch zu würken. Euch neide und hasse alles das reich, das da ist im himel, auf erden und in der helle!

THE PLOWMAN

Chapter Seven

If I could curse you, if I could abuse you, if I could revile you so that worse than evil would befall you, it would be no more than your deserts, for the harm you have done. For great sorrow brings great lamentation; I would not be human if I did not weep for so precious, so godly a gift which none but God can give. Truly I must mourn for evermore; my noble falcon has flown away. Justly do I lament my virtuous wife, for she was of noble birth, rich in honor, beautiful and wise above all her playmates, tall of stature, truthful and moderate in speech, chaste of body, a kind and cheerful companion. I say no more, for I am too weak to recount all the qualities and virtues with which God himself had endowed her. Death, sir, you know it yourself. I am sick at heart, and therefore rightly call you to account. Truly, if there were but a spark of good in you, you would yourself take pity. I shall turn a cold shoulder on you, have nothing good to say of you and forever oppose you with all my might. All God's creation shall stand by my side in striving against you. May it be hostile to you and hate you, the whole kingdom which is in heaven, on earth and in hell!

DER TOD

Das VIII. capitel

Des himels tron den guten geisten, der helle abgrund den bösen, irdische land hat Got uns zu erbeteile gegeben. Dem himel fride und lon nach tugenden, der helle weine und strafung nach sünden, der erden, luft und meres strame mit aller irer behaltung hat unstetigkeit der mechtig aller werlte herzog beschiden und sie uns befolhen, den worten das wir alle überflüssigkeit ausreuten und ausjeten sullen. Nim vür dich, tummer man, prüfe und grab mit sinnes grabestickel in die vernunft, so findestu: hetten wir sider des ersten von leime gekleckten mannes zeit leute auf erden, tiere und würme in wustung und in wilden heiden, schuppentragender und slipferiger fische in dem wage zuwachsung und merung nicht ausgereutet, vor kleinen mücken möchte nu niemand beleiben, vor wolfen törste nu niemand aus. Es würde fressen ein mensche das ander, ein tier das ander, ein jeglich lebendige beschaffung die ander, wan narung würde in gebrechen, die erde würde in zu enge. Er ist tumb, wer beweinet den tod der tötlichen. Laß ab! Die lebendigen mit den lebendigen, die toten mit den toten, als unz her ist gewesen. Bedenke baß, du tummer, was du klagen süllest!

DEATH

Chapter Eight

God has given us for our portion the estates of this earth, as he has given heaven's throne to the good spirits and the abyss of hell to the wicked. The mighty lord of all the world has allotted peace and the reward of virtue to heaven, weeping and the punishment of sins to hell, and mutability to earth, the air, the waters of the sea and all that therein is, and has entrusted them to us, that we may root up and weed out all superfluity. Consider, foolish man, probe and dig into reason with the needle of thought and you will find this: no-one could now exist for little flies, no-one would dare go out for wolves, if we, since the first man was made of clay, had not exterminated the increase and proliferation of men upon the earth, of beasts and creeping things in the desert and the wilderness, of the scaly and slimy fish in the sea. One man would devour the other, one beast the other, every living thing would devour the other, for they would want for food, the earth would become too small for them. How foolish to bewail the death of mortals. Desist! Let the living belong to the living, the dead to the dead, as it has been hitherto. Consider better, fool, the subject of your lament!

DER ACKERMAN

Das VIIII. capitel

Unwiderbringlichen mein höchsten hort han ich verloren; sol ich nicht wesen traurig? Ja, jamerig muß ich bis an mein ende harren, entweret aller freuden! Der milte Got, der mechtige herre, gereche mich an euch, arger traurenmacher! Entenigt habt ir mich aller wünnen, beraubet lieber lebetage, entspenet micheler eren. Michel ere het ich, wann die guten die reinen tochter eugelten mit iren kindern, in reinem neste gefallen. Tot ist die henne, die da auszoch solche hüner. O Got, du gewaltiger herre, wie liebe sach ich mir, wann sie so züchtiges ganges pflag und alle ere bedenken kunde und sie menschliches geslechte do lieblich segente, sprechend: Dank, lob und ere habe die zarte tochter; ir und iren nestlingen günne Got alles gutes! Künde ich darumb Gote volgedanken, werlich ich tet es willichen. Welchen armen man hette er balde so reichlich begabet? Man rede, was man welle: wen Got mit einem reinen, züchtigen und schönen weibe begabet, der ist volkomenlich begabet, und die gabe heißet gabe und ist ein gabe vor aller irdischer auswendiger gabe. O aller gewaltigster himelgrave, wie wol ist dem geschehen, den du mit einem reinen,

THE PLOWMAN

Chapter Nine

I have lost beyond recovery my greatest treasure:
is not that matter for grief? Bereft of all joy, I must
endure in sorrow to my last day. May God Almighty
in His charity revenge me upon you, you bitter
bringer of sadness. You have despoiled me of all delight, robbed me of the dear days of my life, taken
great honor from me. For great honor was mine
when the lords and ladies looked graciously upon
that pure woman and upon her children born in a
pure nest. But she is dead, the mother hen who
brought up those chicks. O God, mighty Lord, how
happy I was when she conducted herself with so
modest a demeanor and had a care for every honor,
and people blessed her kindly and said: thanks,
praise and honor be to this dear daughter, may God
grant His blessings to her and her little ones. Could
I thank God in full measure, indeed I would gladly
do so. What poor man did He ever endow so richly?
Let them say what they like—the man to whom God
gives a pure, modest and lovely wife has a perfect
gift; and the gift is rightly called a gift, and is a gift
of greater price than all the seeming gifts of this
earth. O most mighty Lord of heaven, how fortunate

unvermeiligten gaten hast begatet! Freue dich, er-
samer man, reines weibes, freue dich, reines weib,
ersames mannes; Got gebe euch freude beiden! Was
weiß davon ein tummer man, der aus disem jungbrunnen nie hat getrunken? Allein mir twenglich
herzeleid ist geschehen, dannoch danke ich Got in-
niglich, das ich die unverruketen tochter han erkant. Euch, böser Tod, aller leute feind, sei Got
ewiglich gehessig!

DER TOD

Das X. capitel

Du hast nicht aus der weisheit brunnen getrunken,
das prüfen wir an deinen worten. In der naturen
würken hastu nicht gesehen, in die mischung werlt-
licher stende hastu nicht geluget, in irdische verwandelung hastu nicht gegutzet; ein unverstendig
welf bistu. Merke, wie die leuchtigen rosen und die
starkriechenden lilien in den gerten, wie die krefti-
gen würze und die lustgebenden blumen in den
auen, wie die feststeenden steine und die hoch-
wachsenden baume in wildem gefilde, wie die kraft-
habenden beren und die starkwaltigen lewen in ent-
rischen wustungen, wie die hochmachtigen starken
recken, wie die behenden, abenteurlichen, hochge-
lerten und allerlei meisterschaft wol vermügenden

is the one You have married to a pure, unsullied spouse. Rejoice, honorable man, in your pure wife, and you, pure wife, rejoice in your honorable husband. May God grant joy to you both. What does a fool know of it, who has never drunk of this fountain of youth? Although bitter sorrow has come upon me, yet I thank God with all my heart that this spotless woman was mine. As for you, wicked Death, enemy of all mankind, may God hate you eternally.

DEATH

Chapter Ten

You certainly have not drunk of the fountain of wisdom—that we can tell from what you say. You have not looked into nature's works, you have glimpsed nothing of the intermixture of the world's composition, you have not seen the transformations of this earth, you are an ignorant young cub. Consider how they must all come to nothing, the glowing roses and the strong-scented lilies in the gardens, the fortifying herbs and the delightful flowers of the meadows, the immovable rocks and the lofty trees in the wild plains, the rugged bears and the mighty lions in the dreadful wilderness, the powerful, commanding champions, the quick-witted, eminent, learned men, masters of all arts, and all earthly creatures, no mat-

leute und wie alle irdische creatüre, wie künstig, wie listig, wie stark sie sein, wie lange sie sich enthalten, wie lange sie es treiben, müssen zu nichte werden und verfallen allenthalben. Und wann nu alle menschgeslechte, die gewesen sint, sint oder noch werden, müssen von wesen zu nichtwesen komen, wes solte die gelobte, die du beweinest, genießen, das ir nicht geschehe als andern allen und allen andern als ir? Du selber wirst uns nicht entrinnen, wie wenig du des jetzund getrauest. Alle hernach! muß eur jeglicher sprechen. Dein klage ist enwicht; sie hilfet dich nicht, sie get aus tauben sinnen.

DER ACKERMAN

Das XI. capitel

Got, der mein und eur gewaltig ist, getraue ich wol, er werde mich vor euch beschirmen und umb die verwurkten übeltat, die ir an mir begangen habet, strenglich an euch gerechen. Gaukelweise traget ir mir war under, falsch mischet ir mir ein und wellet mir mein ungeheur sinneleid, vernunftleid und herzeleid aus den augen, aus den sinnen und aus dem mute slahen. Ir schaffet nicht, wan mich reuet mein serige verlust, die ich nimmer widerbringen mag. Vür alles we und ungemach mein heilsame erzenei,

ter how clever, how cunning or how strong they may be, no matter how long they survive nor how long they go on—at last they must all decay, wherever they are. And if all the generations of men that have been, are and shall be, must go from being to not-being, how should the one you praise and mourn be granted a fate different from that of all others, and others one different from hers? You yourself will not escape us, however little you may reckon with it now. First one, then another, every one of you must say. Your plaint is null and void; it does not help you; it proceeds from a dull mind.

THE PLOWMAN

Chapter Eleven

I trust in God, Who has power over me and you, that He will shield me against you and will sternly avenge me upon you for the evil deed that you have done to me. Like a conjurer you trick me by mixing together the true and the false, and you think to drive from my eyes, my head and my heart the vast sorrow that my senses, my mind and my soul have suffered. You cannot do it, for I feel the pain of my hurt, my loss, which can never be made good. Unwearying by day and night, she was my healing

meines gutes dienerin, meines willens pflegerin,
meines leibes auswarterin, meiner eren und irer eren
tegelich und nechtlich wachterin was sie unverdros-
sen. War ir empfolhen ward, das ward von ir ganz
reine und unverseret, oft mit merung widerreichet.
Ere, Zucht, Keusche, Milte, Treue, Maße, Sorge und
Bescheidenheit wonten stete in irem hofe, Scham
trug stete der Eren spiegel vor iren augen. Got was
ir günstiger handhaber. Er was auch mir günstig
und genedig durch iren willen; Heil, Selde und
Gelücke stunden mir bei durch iren willen. Das het
sie an Got erworben und verdienet, die reine hausere. Lon und genedigen sold gib ir, milter loner
aller treuen soldener, aller reichster herre! Tu ir
genediglicher, wan ich ir kan gewünschen! Ach, ach,
ach! unverschamter mörder, herre Tod, böser laster-
balg! Der züchtiger sei eur richter und binde euch,
sprechend: vergib mir!, in sein wigen!

DER TOD

Das XII. capitel

Kündestu rechte messen, wegen, zelen oder tichten,
aus ödem kopge ließestu nicht solche rede. Du flu-
chest und bittest rachung unverfenglich und one
notdurft. Was taug solch eselschrei? Wir haben vor

medicine for all pains and privations, she gave her service for my good, fostered my will, cared for my body and watched over my honor and her own. Whatever was confided to her she returned wholly pure and undamaged, and often in greater measure. Honor, dignity, chastity, charity, loyalty, moderation, loving care and discretion lived always at her court and virtue held the mirror of honor always before her eyes. God in His mercy guarded her. He showed mercy and grace to me also for her sake; health, happiness and fortune stood by my side because of her. She earned it and deserved it of God, she whose virtue ennobled my hearth and home. O bounteous rewarder of all faithful servants, most rich Lord, give her, of Your grace, her wages and her reward. Show her more mercies than I can wish for her! But woe on you, Lord Death, you shameless murderer, you wicked slanderer; may the hangman be your judge and bind you, with the words 'Forgive me,' to his rack.

DEATH

Chapter Twelve

You would not talk in that empty-headed way if you could measure things aright, if you could rightly ponder, count or evaluate. Your cursing and crying down vengeance are useless and groundless. What

gesprochen: künstereich, edel, erhaft, frütig, ertig und alles, was lebet, muß von unserer hende abhendig werden. Dannoch klaffestu und sprichest, alles dein gelücke sei an deinem reinen, frumen weibe gelegen. Sol nach deiner meinung gelücke an weiben ligen, so wellen wir dir wol raten, das du bei gelücke beleibest, den worten das es nicht zu ungelücke gerate! Sage uns: do du am ersten dein löbelich weib namest, fandestu sie frum oder machtestu sie frum? Hastu sie frum funden, so suche vernünftiglichen: du findest noch vil frumer, reiner frauen auf erden, der dir eine zu der e werden mag; hastu sie aber frum gemachet, so freue dich; du bist der lebendig meister, der noch ein frum weib geziehen und gemachen kan. Wir sagen dir aber andere mere: je mer dir liebes wirt, je mer dir leides widerfert. Hettestu dich vor liebes überhaben, so werestu nu leides vertragen; je größer lieb zu bekennen, je größer leid zu enberen. Lieb, weib, kind, schatz und alles irdisch gut muß etwas freuden am anfang haben und mer leides am ende bringen; alles irdisch ding und lieb muß zu leide werden. Leid ist liebes ende, der freuden ende trauren ist, nach lust unlust muß komen, willens ende ist unwillen. Zu solchem ende laufen alle lebendige ding. Lerne es baß, wiltu von klugheit gatzen!

is the good of braying like a jackass? As we said already: whatever is clever, noble, honorable, brave, worthy, indeed, everything that lives, cannot but be undone by our deed. Nevertheless you yelp and say that all your happiness lay in your pure and virtuous wife. If it's your opinion that happiness resides in women, then we can only advise you to stick to that happiness, and may it never make you unhappy! Tell us this: when you first took your estimable wife, did you find her already virtuous, or did you make her virtuous? If you found her virtuous, then be sensible and look about you. You will find in the world many another woman to marry, even more virtuous, even purer. But if you made your wife virtuous, then rejoice, for you are the living master who can educate and make another virtuous wife. However, we have something else to say: the more you love, the more sorrow you lay up for yourself. If you had abstained from love before, you would now be free from sorrow. The greater the love for what one has, the greater the sorrow when it must be given up. Love, wife, child, treasure and all earthly goods give some joy in the beginning but bring far greater sorrow in the end. All earthly things, all love, turn to sorrow. Love ends in sorrow and joy in mourning. After pleasure comes displeasure and wishes conclude in weariness. All living things hasten to this end. Learn that better if you want to cluck so cleverly.

DER ACKERMAN

Das XIII. capitel

Nach schaden folget spotten, des empfinden wol die betrübten. Also geschicht von euch mir beschedigtem manne. Liebes entspenet, leides gewenet habet ir mich; als lange Got wil, muß ich es von euch leiden. Wie stumpf ich bin, wie wenig ich han zu sinnereichen meistern weisheit gezücket, dannoch weiß ich wol, das ir meiner eren rauber, meiner freuden dieb, meiner guten lebetage steler, meiner wünnen vernichter und alles des, das mir wünnesam leben gemachet und gelübet hat, zerstörer seit. Wes sol ich mich nu freuen? Wo sol ich nu trost suchen? Wohin sol ich nu zuflucht haben? Wo sol ich nu heilstet finden? Wo sol ich nu treuen rat holen? Hin ist hin! Alle meine freude ist mir e der zeit verswunden; zu fru ist sie mir entwischet. Alzu schiere habt ir mir enzücket die teuren, die geheuren, wan ir mich zu witwer und meine kinder zu weisen so ungenediglich habet gemachet. Ellende, allein und leides vol beleibe ich von euch unergetzet, besserung kunde mir von euch nach großer missetat noch nie widerfaren. Wie ist dem, herre Tod, aller e brecher? An euch kan niemand icht gutes verdienen noch finden; nach untat wellet ir niemand genug

40

THE PLOWMAN

Chapter Thirteen

Insult is heaped on injury, as the afflicted well know.
That's your way with me, injured as I am. You have
weaned me from love and fed me on sorrow; I must
bear it from you as long as it be God's will. However
dull I may be, however little wisdom I may have ac-
quired from clever masters, yet I know well that you
have robbed me of my honor, have stolen my joy,
plundered all the good days of my life, undone my
delight and destroyed all that gave and vouchsafed
me a life of bliss. At what shall I now rejoice? Where
shall I seek consolation? Where shall I take refuge?
Where shall I find sanctuary? Where shall I get
good counsel? Gone, all gone. All my joy is vanished
before its time; it has fled from me too soon. All too
swiftly you tore from me my fair beloved when un-
mercifully you made me a widower and my children
orphans. Wretched, lonely and full of sorrow I remain, without amends from you; I could never ob-
tain reparation from you for your grievous crime.
How about that, Death, sir, you wrecker of all mar-
riages? No-one can get or receive anything good
from you; you will give nobody satisfaction for your
ill-doing, will make no compensation. The quality

tun, niemand wellet ir ergetzen. Ich prüfe, barm-
herzigkeit wonet bei euch nicht; fluchens seit ir ge-
wonet; genadenlos seit ir an allen orten. Solche guttat, so ir beweiset an den leuten, solche genade, so
die leute von euch empfahen, solchen lon, so ir den
leuten gebet, solche ende, so ir den leuten tut,
schicke euch der, der des todes und lebens gewaltig
ist. Fürste himelischer massenei, ergetze mich unge-
heurer verluste, michels schadens, unsegeliches
trübsals und jemerliches weisentums! Dabei gerich
mich an dem erzschalke Tod, God, aller untat
gerecher!

DER TOD

Das XIIII. capitel

One nutz geredet, als mer geswigen, wan nach tör-
licher rede krieg, nach kriege feindschaft, nach
feindschaft unrue, nach unrue serung, nach serunge
wetag, nach wetage afterreue muß jedem verworren
manne begegnen. Krieges mutestu uns an. Du kla-
gest, wie wir dir leid haben getan an deiner zumale
lieben frauen. Ir ist gütlich und genediglich geschehen. Bei frölicher jugend, bei stolzem leibe, in besten lebetagen, in besten wirden, an bester zeit, mit
ungekrenkten eren haben wir sie in unser genade
empfangen. Das haben gelobet, das haben begeret

of mercy, I can see, is not in you. You are accustomed to being cursed; at all times and places you are pitiless. May He who has power over life and death, may He send you such mercy as men receive from you, such reward as you give to men, and such an end as you bring them. O prince of the heavenly hosts, make good to me the enormity of my loss, the great injury, the inexpressible misery and woeful bereavement! Avenge me, God, avenger of all evil, upon that arch-villain Death.

DEATH

Chapter Fourteen

Silence is better than vain talk, for a muddled man will find that after foolish talk comes a dispute; after a dispute comes enmity; after enmity, trouble; after trouble, injury; after injury, suffering; after suffering, remorse. You seek a dispute with us. You complain that we have brought sorrow upon you through your most beloved wife. But she has been treated kindly and mercifully. We have received her into our mercy in the gaiety of youth, in the pride of the flesh, in the finest days of her life, in the highest dignity, at the best time, with her honor inviolate. This

alle weissagen, wan sie sprachen: am besten zu sterben, wann am besten liebet zu leben. Er ist nicht wol gestorben, wer sterben hat begeret; er hat zu lange gelebet, wer uns umb sterben hat angerufet. We und ungemach geschach im, wer mit alters bürden wirt überladen: bei allem reichtum muß er arm wesen! Des jares, do die himelfart offen was, an des himels torwertels kettenfeirtag, do man zalte von anfang der werlte sechstausend fünfhundert neun und neunzig jar, bei kindes geburt tausend vierhundert der selbigen, die seligen martrerin hießen wir raumen dis kurze schemende ellende, auf die meinung das sie solte zu Gotes erbe in ewige freude, in immerwerendes leben und zu unendiger rue nach gutem verdienen genediglichen komen. Wie hessig du uns bist, wir wellen dir wünschen und günnen, das dein sele mit der iren dort in himelischer wonung, dein leib mit dem iren bein bei beine alhie in erden gruft wesen solten. Bürge wolten wir dir werden, irer guttat würdestu genießen. Sweig, enthalt! Als wenig du kanst der sunnen ir licht, dem mone seine kelte, dem feur sein hitze oder dem wasser sein nesse benemen, als wenig kanstu uns unserer macht berauben!

is what all philosophers have praised and desired, for they have said that a man dies best when he most fervently wishes to live. He who desired to die has not made a good death; he who appealed to us for death has lived too long. Pains and privations came to him who was heavily laden with the burden of age; he was poor whatever his wealth. In the year when the way to heaven was open, on the feast of St. Peter's Chains, when the years since the beginning of the world numbered 6,599 and those since the birth of the child Jesus numbered 1,400, we caused the blessed martyr to leave this brief, bright exile, with the intent that she who had deserved so well should come by grace into the inheritance of God, into eternal joy, into life everlasting and peace without end. Despite the hatred you bear us, we will gladly wish and concede that your soul may dwell with hers in the heavenly mansions and that your body may rest with hers, bone to bone, in your grave here on earth. We meant to vouchsafe you the benefit of her virtue. Don't say a word! You can as little deprive us of our power as you can take from the sun its light, from the moon its cold, from fire its heat or from water its wetness.

DER ACKERMAN
Das XV. capitel

Beschonter rede bedarf wolf schuldiger man. Also tut ir auch. Süße und saur, linde und herte, gütig und scharf pfleget ir euch zu beweisen den, die ir meinet zu betriegen. Das ist offen an mir schein worden. Wie sere ir euch beschönet, doch weiß ich, das ich der erenvollen, durchschönen von eurer swinden ungenade wegen kümmerlich enberen muß. Auch weß ich wol, das solches gewaltes sunder Got und eur niemand ist gewaltig. So bin ich von Gote nicht also geplaget: wan hette ich mißgebaret gen Gote, als leider dicke geschehen ist, das hette er an mir gerochen, odes es hette mir widerbracht die wandelsone. Ir seit der übelteter. Darumb weste ich gern, wer ir weret, was ir weret, wie ir weret, von wann ir weret und warzu ir tüchtig weret, das ir so vil gewaltes habet und one entsagen mich also übel gefodert, meinen wünnereicher anger geödet, meiner sterke turn undergraben und gefellet habet. Ach Got, aller betrübten herzen tröster, tröste mich und ergetze mich armen, betrübten, ellenden, selbsitzenden man! Gib, herre, plage, tu widerwerte, leg an klemnüß und vertilge den greulichen Tod, der dein und aller unser feind ist! Werlich, herre, in deiner würkung ist nicht greulichers, nicht, scheuß-

THE PLOWMAN
Chapter Fifteen

A guilty man needs to use fair words. And so do you.
Sweet and sour, mild and harsh, kind and sharp—
such is your way with those you mean to deceive.
My case has made it clear. Whatever gloss you put
on it, I know all the same that I must sadly live without my honored and lovely one because of your
merciless severity. I know, too, that apart from God
and you no-one commands such power. Yet it is not
by God that I am thus tormented, for either He
would have punished me myself for my sins which,
alas, have been many, or He would have forgiven
them on account of my spotless wife. The evil-doer
is you. Therefore I would like to know who you are,
what you are, how you are, whence you come and
what purpose you serve, that you should have such
power, that without warning you should so wick-
edly have made war on me, laid waste my field of
delight, undermined the tower of my strength and
overthrown it. O God, consoler of the broken-
hearted, console me and comfort me, poor, grieving,
wretched lonely man that I am. And, Lord, send
down torment and retribution upon cruel Death,
Your enemy and the enemy of us all; fetter him and
exterminate him. For see, Lord, in all Your creation

lichers, nicht schedlichers, nicht herbers, nicht ungerechters dann der Tod! Er betrübet und verrüret dir alle dein irdische herschaft; e das tüchtig dann das untüchtig nimt er hin; schedliche, alte, sieche, unnütze leute lesset er oft alhie, die guten und die nützen zücket er alle hin. Richte, herre, rechte über den falschen richter!

DER TOD

Das XVI. capitel

Was böse ist, das nennen gut, was gut ist, das heißen böse sinnelose leute. Dem gleiche tustu auch. Falsches gerichtes zeihestu uns; uns tustu unrecht. Des wellen wir dich underweisen. Dru fragest, wer wir sein. Wir sein Gotes handgezeuge, herre Tod, ein rechte würkender meder. Unser segens get vür sich. Weiß, swarz, rot, braun, grün, blau, grau, gel und allerlei glanzes blumen unde gras heuet sie vür sich nider, ires glanzes, irer kraft, irer tugend nicht geachtet. Da geneußet der veiol nicht seiner schönen farbe, seines reichen ruches, seiner wolsmeckender safte. Sich, das its rechtfertigkeit. Uns haben rechtfertig geteilet die Römer und die poeten, wan sie uns baß dann du bekanten. Du fragest, was wir sein. Wir sein nichts und sein doch etwas. Deshalben nichts, wan wir weder leben weder wesen, noch ge-

there is nothing more cruel, more horrible, more dreadful, more bitter and more unjust than Death. He disturbs and confuses Your rule on earth; he carries off the worthy rather than the unworthy; evil-doing, old, ill, useless people he often spares while he sweeps away the good and the useful. Give Your just judgment, Lord, upon the false judge!

DEATH

Chapter Sixteen

Fools call good what is wicked, and wicked what is good. You do the same. You accuse us of false judgment, you do us an injustice. We will prove it to you. You ask who we are. We are God's instrument, the Lord Death, a trusty reaper. Our scythe sweeps straight before it. It lays low the grasses and the flowers of every hue, the light and the dark, the red, purple, green, blue, the grey and the golden, without regard for their glory, their strength or their virtue. The violet has no profit from its beautiful color, its rich perfume, its delicious essence. That, you see, is justice. The Romans and the poets judged us just, because they knew us better than you do. You ask what we are. We are nothing and yet we are something. Nothing, because we have neither life nor being, neither shape nor condition, are not spirit,

stalt noch understand haben, nicht geis sein, nicht sichtig sein, nicht greiflich sein; deshalben etwas, wan wir sein des lebens ende, des wesens ende, des nichtwesens anfang, ein mittel zwischen in beiden. Wir sein ein geschickte, das alle leute fellet. Die großen heunen musten vor uns fallen; alle wesen, die leben haben, müssen verwandelt von uns werden; in hohen schulden werden wir gesigen. Du fragest, wie wir sein. Unbescheidenlich sein wir, wan unser figure zu Rome in einem tempel an einer wand gemalet was als ein man sitzend auf einem ochsen, dem die augen verbunden waren. Der selbe man furte ein hauen in seiner rechten hand und ein schaufel in der linken hand; damit facht er auf dem ochsen. Gegen im slug, warf und streit ein michel menige volkes. Allerlei leute, jegliches mensche mit seines handwerkes gezeuge—da was auch die nunne mit dem psalter—, die slugen und wurfen den man auf dem ochsen. In unser bedeutnüß bestreit der und begrub sie alle. Pictura gleichet uns zu eines mannes scheine, der hat basilisken augen, vor des gesichte sterben muß alle lebendige creatüre. Du fragest, von wann wir sein. Wir sein von allenthalben und sein doch von ninder. Deshalben von allenthalben, wan wir wandern an allen enden der werlte; deshalben von ninder, wan wir sein ninder her komen und aus nichte. Wir sein von dem irdischen paradise. Da tirmete uns Got und nante uns mit unserem rechten namen, do er sprach zu dem ersten menschen: Welches tages ir der frucht en-

cannot be seen nor touched; yet something, because we are the end of life, the end of being, the beginning of not-being, a mean between the two. We are a destiny that fells all men. Mighty giants must fall before us; all beings that have life must be transformed by us; we shall rightly prevail. You ask how we are. We are not to be described, although in Rome on the wall of a temple we were painted as a man sitting on an ox, with eyes blindfolded. In his right hand the man carried a hoe and in his left a spade, and with these he fought on the ox. A great throng of people struck at him, belabored him and pelted him. All kinds of people, each with the tools of his trade—even a nun with her psalter was there —struck and pelted the man on the ox. But in our likeness he fought and buried them all. Legend has it that we are a man with basilisk eyes at whose gaze all living creatures must die. You ask whence we come. We come from everywhere and yet from nowhere. From everywhere because we have wandered to all the ends of the earth; from nowhere because we have come hither from nowhere and out of nothing. We come from the earthly paradise. God created us there and named us by our right name when He said to the first man: in the day that thou eatest of the fruit thou shalt surely die. Therefore we sign ourself: We, Death, lord and master upon earth, in the air and in the waters of the sea. You ask what purpose we serve. Now you have heard that we do the world more good than harm. So stop, be satisfied

beißet, des todes werdet ir sterben. Darumb wir uns also schreiben: Wir Tod, herre und gewaltiger auf erden, in der luft und meres strame. Du fragest, warzu wir tüchtig sein. Nu hastu vor gehöret, das wir der werlte mer nutzes dann unnutzes bringen. Hör auf, laß dich genügen und danke uns, das dir von uns so gütlich ist geschehen!

DER ACKERMAN

Das XVII. capitel

Alter man neue mere, geleret man unbekante mere, ferre gewandert man und einer, wider den niemand reden tar, gelogen mere wol sagen turren, wan sie von unwissender sachen wegen sint unstreflich. Wann ir dann auch ein solcher alter man seit, so müget ir wol tichten. Allein ir in dem paradise gefallen seit ein meder und rechtes remet, doch heuet eur segens uneben. Rechte mechtig blumen reutet sie aus, die distel lesset sie sten; unkraut beleibet, die guten kreuter müssen verderben. Ir jehet, eur segens haue vür sich. Wie ist dann dem, das sie mer distel dann guter blumen, mer meuse dann zamer tiere, mer böser leute dann guter unverseret lesset beleiben? Nennet mir mit dem munde, mit dem finger weiset mir: wo sint die frumen, achtberen leute, als vor zeinen waren? Ich wene, ir habet sie hin.

and thankful that you have been so well treated by us.

THE PLOWMAN

Chapter Seventeen

An old man may tell new tales, a learned man may tell unknown tales, a widely travelled man and one against whom none dares to speak, may tell lying tales, because ignorance saves them from penalty. If you are that sort of old man, it is easy for you to romance. Even if you were created in paradise as a reaper and mean to do right, none the less your scythe cuts unfairly. It lops off the most splendid flowers and spares the thistles; weeds remain and the good herbs are destroyed. You say that your scythe sweeps straight before it. How is it then that it leaves untouched more thistles than useful flowers, more vermin than domestic animals, more wicked folk than good? Tell me plainly and point out with your finger where they are now, the virtuous and worthy people who lived in earlier times. I believe

53

Mit in ist auch mein lieb, die übeln sint joch über beliben. Wo sint sie hin, die auf erden wonten und mit Gote redeten, an im hulde, genade und rechtung erwurben? Wo sint sie hin, die auf erden saßen under der gestirne umbgengen und entschieden die planeten? Wo sint sie hin, die sinnereichen, die meisterlichen, die gerechten, die frütigen leute, von den die kroniken so vil sagen? Ir habet sie alle und mein zarte ermordet; die snöden sint noch alda. Wer ist daran schuldig? Törstet ir der wahrheit bekennen, herre Tod, ir würdet euch selber nennen. Ir sprechet faste, wie rechte ir richtet, niemandes schonet, eurer segense hau nach einander fellet. Ich stund dabei und sach mit meinen augen zwo ungeheure schar volkes — jede het über dreitausend man — mit einander streiten auf einer grünen heide; die wuten in dem blute bis under den waden. Darunder snurretet ir und burretet gar gescheftig an allen enden. In dem here totetet ir etelich, etelich ließet ir sten. Minre knechte dann herren sach ich tot ligen. Do klaubetet ir einen aus den andern als die teigen biren. Ist das rechte gemet? Is das rechte gerichtet? Get so eur segens vür sich? Wol her, lieben kinder, wol her! Reiten wir engegen, enbieten und sagen wir lob und ere dem Tode, der also rechte richtet! Gotes gerichte ist kaum also gerecht!

you have taken them all away. And with them my darling; only the wicked are left behind. Where have they gone, who once dwelt on earth and spoke with God and gained from Him grace, favor and mercy? Where have they gone who rested on earth, under the circling stars, and determined the paths of the planets? Where have they gone, all those of whom the chronicles tell so much, all the sages, the masters, the just, the brave? You have murdered them all and my dearest too. The base remain. Who is to blame for that? If you dared admit the truth, Lord Death, you would name yourself. You insist on how justly you judge, how you spare none, how your scythe cuts one after another. I stood by and saw with my own eyes two great hosts—each numbered more than three thousand—that were battling upon a green heath. They were wading in blood up to their ankles. You were among them, as busy as could be, roaring and rushing from side to side. In the army you killed some and some you left standing. I saw fewer men lying dead than officers. You were culling the ones from the others like sleepy pears. Is that to reap justly? Is that to judge justly? Is that how your scythe sweeps straight before it? Here, children, here! Let us ride up and salute Death and give him praise and honor, Death who judges so justly. Even the judgment of God is barely as just.

DER TOD

Das XVIII. capitel

Wer von sachen nicht enweiß, der kan von sachen
nicht gesagen. Also ist uns auch geschehen. Wir
westen nicht, das du als ein richtiger man werest.
Wir haben dich lange zeit erkant, wir hetten aber
dein vergessen. Wir waren dabei, do frau Sibilla dir
die weisheit mitteilte, do her Salomon an dem tot-
bette dir sein weisheit verreichte; do Got allen den
gewalt, den er hern Moysi in Egipten land verlihen
het, dir verlech, do du einen lewen bei dem weinwachs von Thamnatha slugest. Wir sahen dich die
sterne zelen, des meres grieß und sein fische rech-
nen, die regentropfen reiten. Wir sahen gern, das du
gewanst den wetlauf an Asael. Zu Susan sahen wir
dich koste und trank in großen wirden credenzen.
Do du das banier vor Alexandro furtest, do er Da-
rium bestreit, do lugten wir zu und gunden dir wol
der eren. Do du in Academia zu Athenis mit hohen
künstereichen meistern, die auch in die gotheit meisterlichen sprechen kunden, ebenteure disputiertest
und in so künstelichen oblagest, do sahen wir uns
zumale liebe. Do du Neronem underweisetest, das
er guttete und gedultig wesen solte, do horten wir
gütlichen zu. Uns wunderte, do du keiser Iulium in

DEATH

Chapter Eighteen

One cannot talk about something one does not know.
That is how it is with us. We had no idea you were
such a splendid fellow. We have known you for a
long time, but we had forgotten you. We were there
when the Sybil told you her wisdom, when Solomon
on his death bed handed over his wisdom to you,
when God granted you all the power he had granted
Moses in the land of Egypt, when you slew a lion in
the vineyards of Timnath. We saw you tell the num-
ber of the stars and of the sands and the fish of the
sea, we saw you reckon up the raindrops. Gladly we
saw you win the race with Asahel. In Shushan we
saw you make a feast, in great honor. When you
bore the standard of Alexander in his battle with
Darius, we looked on and did not grudge you the
honor. We rejoiced especially when at the academy
in Athens you disputed on a level of equality with
distinguished men of learning, masters of theologi-
cal discussion, and brilliantly carried the day. We
listened with pleasure when you instructed Nero
that he should do good and be patient. We mar-
velled when you took Julius Caesar in a vessel of
bulrushes over the wild sea, unmindful of the storm.

einem rören schiffe über das wilde mer furtest one dank aller sturmwinde. In deiner werkstat sahen wir dich ein edel gewand von regenbogen würken; darein wurden engel, vogel, tier, fische under allerlei gestalt — da was auch die eule und her affe — in wefels weise getragen. Zumale sere lachten wir und wurden des vür dich rümig, do du zu Paris auf dem gelückes rade saßest, auf der heute tantetest, in der swarzen kunst wurketest und bannetest die teufel in ein seltsam glas. Do dich Got berufte in seinen rat zu gespreche umb frauen Eve fal, aller erste wurden wir deiner großen weisheit innen. Hetten wir dich vor erkant, wir hetten dir gefolget, wir hetten dein weib und alle leute ewig lassen leben. Das hetten wir dir allein zu eren getan, wan du bist zemale ein kluger esel!

DER ACKERMAN

Das XVIIII. capitel

Gespötte und übelhandelung müssen dicke aufhalten durch warheit willen die leute. Gleicher weise geschicht mir. Unmügelicher dinge rümet ir mich, ungehorter werke würkens. Gewaltes treibet ir zumale vil, gar übel habt ir an mir gefaren, das müet mich auzl sere. Wann ich dann darumb rede, so seit ir mir gehessig und werdet zornes vol. Wer

We saw you in your workshop when you were weaving a magnificent garment out of a rainbow: angels, birds, beasts, fish and all kinds of creatures—the owl and the ape among them—were worked into it. Most especially did we laugh and applaud you when in Paris you sat upon Fortune's wheel and danced upon the hide and used black magic and enclosed the devil in a curious glass. The very first time we became aware of your great wisdom was when God called on you to speak at His council on the fall of Eve. If we had recognized you earlier, we would have followed your lead, we would have let your wife and everyone live for ever. We would have done that solely on your account, for you really are a clever ass!

THE PLOWMAN

Chapter Nineteen

For the sake of truth men often have to endure mockery and ill-treatment. That is how it is with me. You praise me for impossible things, for doing unheard-of deeds. You yourself wield great power and have done me great harm, that causes me all too much pain. If I speak about it, you bear me ill-will and get very angry. Let him who does evil, and will

übel tut und wil nicht undertan strafung aufnemen und leiden, sunder mit übermut alle ding vertreiben, der sol gar eben aufsehen, das im nicht unwillen darnach begegne! Nemet beispil bei mir! Wie zu kurze, wie zu lange, wie ungütlich, wie unrechte ir mir mit habet gefaren, dannoch dulte ich und riche es nicht, als ich zu rechte solte. Noch heute wil ich des besserer sein, han ich icht ungleiches oder unhübsches gen euch gebaret. Des underweiset mich; ich wil sein gernwilliglich widerkomen. Ist des aber nicht, so ergetzet mich meines schadens oder underweiset mich, wie ich widerkome meines großen herzeleides. Werlich, also zu kurze geschach nie manner! Über das alles mein bescheidenheit sullet ir je sehen. Eintweder ir widerbringet, was ir an meiner traurenwenderin, an mir und an meinen kindern arges habet begangen, oder komet des mit mir an Got, der da ist mein, eur und aller werlte rechter richter. Ir möchtet mich leichte erbitten, ich wolte es zu euch selber lassen. Ich traute euch wol, ir würdet eur ungerechtigkeit selber erkennen, darnach mir genügen tun nach großer untat. Beget die bescheidenheit, anders es müste der hamer den amboß treffen, herte wider herte wesen, es kome, zu wo es kome!

not humbly take punishment and bear it, but haughtily resists everything, let him pay due heed lest wrath come upon him thereafter. Take an example from me. However you have treated me, whether your ways were too curt or too long, however badly or unjustly, I have borne it and not taken revenge as I rightly should. This very day I will make it up if I have ever behaved in an unseemly or discourteous way toward you. Only let me know, and I will willingly make amends. But if it is not so, then make good my injury, or teach me how to cure my heartache. Never, indeed, was a man so ill-used. But in spite of everything you shall acknowledge my moderation. Either make good all the harm you have done to the averter of my sorrows, to me and my children, or come with me before God Who is the just judge of me and you and all the world. I am easy to persuade; I would leave it to you yourself. I am ready to trust you to admit your injustice and accordingly repair the great wrong done to me. Be reasonable, or else the hammer must strike the anvil —iron on iron, come what may.

DER TOD

Das XX. capitel

Mit guter rede werden gesenftet die leute; bescheidenheit behelt die leute bei gemache; gedult bringet die leute zu eren; zorniger man kan den man nicht entscheiden. Hettestu uns vormals gütlich zugesprochen, wir hetten dich gütlich underweiset, das du nicht billich den tod deines weibes klagen soltest und beweinen. Hastu nicht gekant Senecam den weissagen, der in dem bade sterben wolte, oder seine bücher gelesen, das niemand sol klagen den tod der tötlichen? Weistu des nicht, so wisse: als balde ein mensche geboren wirt, als balde hat es den leikauf getrunken, das es sterben sol. Anfanges gewistreit ist das ende. Wer ausgesant wirt, der ist pflichtig wider zu komen. Was je geschehen sol, des sol sich niemand widern. Was alle leute leiden müssen, das sol einer nicht widersprechen. Was ein mensche entlehent, das sol es widergeben. Ellende bauen all leute auf erden. Von ichte zu nichte müssen sie werden. Auf snellem fuße leufet hin der menschen leben; jetzund lebend, in einem handwenden gestorben. Mir kurtzer rede beslossen: jedes mensche ist uns ein sterben schuldig und es anerbet zu sterben. Beweinestu aber deines weibes jugend,

DEATH

Chapter Twenty

A soft answer turneth away wrath; sweet reasonableness puts people at their ease; patience honors people; an angry man cannot deal fairly with his neighbor. If you had spoken gently to us before, we would have gently taught you that rightfully you should not lament and bewail your wife's death. Have you not heard of the philosopher Seneca who wanted to die in his bath, or read in his books that nobody should lament a mortal's death? If you do not know it already, then learn now that every man in the moment of birth swallows the drink which pledges his death. Beginning and end are kith and kin. Who is sent forth is bound to come home. No-one may resist what must happen in the end. The individual may not oppose what all must endure. What a man borrows he must return. On earth all men till an alien soil. From being something they must become nothing. Men's lives flee swiftly away. Though they be yet living, in the twinkling of an eye they are dead. To conclude in a word: every man owes us a death and dying is his inheritance. You do wrong to mourn your wife's youth; as soon as a man comes into this life he is old enough to die.

dun tust unrecht; also schiere ein mensche lebendig wirt, als schiere ist es alt genug zu sterben. Du meinest leichte, das alter sei ein edel hort. Nein, es ist süchtig, arbeitsam, ungestalt, kalt und allen leuten übel gefallend; es taug nicht und ist zu allen sachen enwicht: zeitig epfel fallen gern in das kot; reifende biren fallen gern in die pfützen. Klagestu dann ir schöne, du tust kindlich; eines jeglichen menschen schöne muß eintweder das alter oder der tod vernichten. Alle rosenfarbe mündlein müssen abgefarb werden, alle rote wenglein müssen bleich werden, alle lichte euglein müssen tunkel werden. Hastu nicht gelesen, wie Ieronimus, der weissage, leret, wie sich ein man hüten sol vor schönen weiben, und spricht: Was schöne ist, das ist mit tegelicher beisorge sware zu halten, wan sein alle leute begeren; was scheußlich ist, das ist leidelich zu halten, wan es mißfellet allen leuten? Laß faren! Klage nicht verlust, die du nicht kanst widerbringen.

DER ACKERMAN

Das XXI. capitel

Gute strafung gütlich aufnemen, darnach tun sol weiser man, höre ich die klugen jehen. Eur strafung ist auch leidelich. Wann dann ein guter strafer auch ein guter anweiser wesen sol, so ratet und under-

Perhaps you think that age is a precious treasure. Not so; it is sick, wearisome, ill-favored, cold and displeasing to all men. It is worthless and useless for everything. An apple when its season is come falls gladly into the mire, a ripe pear into the puddle. But to lament her beauty is childish. Either age or death must destroy all human beauty. Rosy lips must lose their color, red cheeks must pale, bright eyes must dim. Have you not read what Jerome the philosopher teaches, namely, that a man should beware of beautiful women? He says that whatever is beautiful brings cares day in, day out, and is hard to keep, for all men desire it, whereas what is ugly is easy to keep, for it displeases everyone. Let things take their course. Do not lament a loss which you cannot recover.

THE PLOWMAN

Chapter Twenty-one

A wise man should take a good reproof in good part, the sages say. And your reproof can be borne. If it should happen that one who reproves well also instructs well, then advise me and teach me how I am

weiset mich, wie ich so unsegeliches leid, so jemerlichen kummer, so aus der maße großs betrübnüß
aus dem herzen, aus dem mute und aus den sinnen
ausgraben, austilgen unde ausjagen sülle. Bei Got,
unvolsagenlich herzeleid ist mir geschehen, do mein
züchtige, treue und state hausere mir so snelle ist
enzücket, sie tot, ich witwer, meine kinder weisen
worden sint. O herre Tod, all werlt klaget über euch
und auch ich, das nie so böser man ward. Doch seint
den malen das nie man so böse ward, er were an
etwe gut, ratet, helfet und steuret, wie ich so sweres
leid von herzen werfen müge und meine kinder
einer solchen reinen muter ergetzet werden; anders
ich unmutig und sie traurig immer wesen müssen.
Und das sullet ir mit nichten übel verfahen, wan ich
sihe, das under unvernünftigen tieren ein gate umb
des andern tod trauret von angeborenem twange.
Hilfe, rates und widerbringens seit ir mir pflichtig,
wan ir habt mir getan den schaden. Wo des nicht
geschehe, dann Got hette in seiner almechtigkeit
ninder rachung. Gerochen muß es werden inder,
und solte darumb haue und schaufel noch eines ge-
müet werden!

to dig out, exterminate and drive away from my heart, spirit and mind such unutterable sorrow, such woeful grief, and affliction so unbounded. By God, a heart-ache that cannot be told came to me when the honor of my home, its dignity, truth and constancy, were so suddenly snatched from me, when she died, when I became a widower and my children orphans. O Death, sir, all the world complains, and I with it, that never was such a wicked man as you. Yet since there is no man so wicked but has some good in him, advise me, help me and show me how I can lift such heavy sorrow from my heart and how so virtuous a mother can be made good to my children. Otherwise I can only despair and they remain sad for ever. You should not take this amiss, for I see that even among the unreasoning beasts one spouse laments the death of the other, such is the power of inborn instinct. You owe me help, counsel and reparation, for you have done me wrong. If that were not so, then God in His almighty power could never be avenged. But vengeance must be, even if hoe and spade have to be wielded once again.

DER TOD

Das XXII. capitel

Ga! ga! ga! snatert die gans, lamb! lamb! sprichet
der wolf, man predige, was man welle. Solch faden-
richt spinnest auch du. Wir haben dir vor entwor-
fen, das unklegelich wesen sülle der tod der tötlichen. Seint den malen das wir ein zolner sein, dem
alle menschen ir leben zollen und vermauten müssen, wes widerstu dann dich? Wan werlich, wer uns
teuschen wil, der teuschet sich selber. Laß dir eingen und vernim: das leben ist durch sterbens willen
geschaffen. Were leben nicht, wir weren nicht, unser
geschefte were nicht; damit were auch nicht der
werlte ordenung. Eintweder du bist ser leidig oder
unvernunft hauset zu dir. Bistu unvernünftig, so
bitte Got, vernunft dir zu verleihen; bistu aber leidig, so brich ab, laß faren, nim das vür dich, das ein
wind ist der leute leben auf erden! Du bittest rat,
wie du leid aus dem herzen bringen süllest. Aristo-
tiles hat dich es vor geleret, das freude, leid, forchte
und hoffenung die viere alle werlt bekümmern und
gerlich die, die sich vor in nicht künnen hüten.
Freude und forchte kürzen, leid und hoffenung
lengen die weile. Wir die viere nicht ganz aus dem
mute treibet, der muß alzeit sorgende wesen. Nach

DEATH

Chapter Twenty-two

Quack! quack! gobbles the goose; lamb! lamb! says the wolf, no matter what one preaches to them. You go by the same rule. As we have previously expounded to you, the death of mortals should not be mourned. In as much as we are the toll-keeper to whom all men must pay their life's toll and duty, why do you resist? Those who try to cheat us cheat only themselves. Take hold of this and understand it—life is created for the sake of death. Were there no life, we would not exist, nor our handiwork, and as a result there would be no order in the world. You must either be in great sorrow or in the grip of unreason. If you want for reason, then beg God to grant it to you. But if you sorrow, then have done with it, let things take their course, and remember that man's life on earth is but a puff of wind. You ask advice on how to rid your heart of sorrow. Aristotle has already taught you that these four, joy, sorrow, fear and hope, bring affliction on all the world and especially on those who cannot guard against them. Joy and fear shorten time and sorrow and hope lengthen it. Care will always burden the man who cannot wholly free his spirit of these four.

freude trübsal, nach liebe leid muß je auf erden komen. Lieb und leid müssen mit einander wesen. Eines ende ist anfang des andern. Leid und lieb ist nicht anders, dann wann icht ein mensche in seinen sinn vürfasset, das es nicht austreiben wil, gleicher weise als mit genügen niemand arm und mit ungenügen niemand reich wesen mag; wan genügen und ungenügen nicht an habe noch an auswendigen sachen sint, sunder in dem mute. Wer altes lieb nicht aus dem herzen treiben wil, der muß gegenwürtiges leid alzeit tragen. Treib aus dem herzen, aus dem sinne und aus dem mute liebes gedechtnüß, alzuhand wirstu traurens überhaben. Als balde du icht hast verloren und es nicht kanst widerbringen, tu, als es dein nie sei worden: hin fleuchet alzuhand dein trauren. Wirstu des nicht tun, so hastu mer leides vor dir; wan nach jegliches kindes tode widerfert dir herzeleid, nach deinem tode auch herzeleid in allen, dir und in, wann ir euch scheiden sullet. Du wilt, das sie der muter ergetzet werden. Kanstu vergangene jar, gesprochene wort und verrucketen magettum widerbringen, so widerbringestu die muter deiner kinder. Wir haben dir genug geraten. Kanstau es versten, stumpfer pickel?

Here on earth sadness must always come after joy and sorrow after love. These two must keep company. The end of one is the other's beginning. It is with sorrow and love as when a man has something in his mind and refuses to give it up; in the same way, with content nobody is poor and with discontent nobody is rich, for content and discontent have to do not with possessions and outward things, but with the spirit. Whoever will not drive old love out of his heart, must always bear present sorrow. Drive the memory of love out of your heart, mind and spirit, and you will at once be relieved of grief. As soon as you have lost something and cannot get it back, act as though it had never been yours, and at once your grief will flee away. If you will not do that, then you have more sorrow to come. For after every child's death you will suffer heart-ache, and so will they all, after your death, they and you, when you have to part from one another. You want their mother to be replaced for them. If you can bring back past years, and words that have been spoken and deflowered maidenheads, then you can restore their mother to your children. We have given you enough advice. Can you understand it, blockhead?

DER ACKERMAN

Das XXIII. capitel

In die lenge wirt man gewar der warheit als: lange
gelernet, etwas gekundet. Eur sprüche sint süße und
lustig, des ich nu etwas empfinde. Doch solte freude,
lieb, wünne und kurzweil aus der werlte vertriben
werden, übel würde sten die werlt. Des wil ich mich
ziehen an die Römer. Die haben es selbes getan und
haben das ire kinder geleret, das sie lieb und in eren
haben solten turnieren, stechen, tanzen, wetlaufen,
springen und allerlei züchtige hübscheit bei müßi-
ger weile, auf die rede das sie die weile bosheit
weren überhaben. Wan menschliches mutes sin kan
nicht müßig wesen. Eintweder gut oder böse muß
alzeit der sin würken; in dem slafe wil er nicht müßig sein. Würden dann dem sinne gute gedanke be-
nomen, so würden im böse eingen. Gute aus, böse
ein; böse aus, gute ein: die wechselung muß bis an
das ende der werlte weren. Sider freude, zucht,
scham und ander hübscheit sint aus der werlte vertriben, sider ist sie bosheit, schanden, untreue, ge-
spöttes und verreterei zumale vol worden. Das sehet
ir tegelichen. Solte ich dann die gedechtüß meiner
aller liebsten aus dem sinne treiben, böse gedecht-
nüsse würden mir in den sin wider komen: als mer

THE PLOWMAN

Chapter Twenty-three

After a time one sees that it is true what they say, that long study brings understanding. Your sayings are sweet and pleasant; I begin to see that now. But if joy, love, delight and mirth were driven from the world, then the world would be in a bad way. I will call the Romans to witness on that. They themselves did what they taught their children, namely, they held in high regard gymnastics, fencing, dancing, running, jumping and every kind of decent amusement in their leisure time, so as to save them from wickedness. For man's mind cannot be idle. Either good or evil must exercise it always; even in sleep it does not want to be idle. If good thoughts are taken away from the mind, evil ones will enter. Out with the good, in with the bad; out with the bad, in with the good. This alternation will last till the end of the world. Since joy, dignity, modesty and other courtly virtues were expelled from the world, it has become brimful with wickedness, disgrace, disloyalty, mockery and treachery. You see it every day. If I were to drive from my mind the memory of my dear darling, evil memories would come back into my mind. With all the more reason shall I always remember my be-

wil ich meiner aller liebsten alweg gedenken. Wann großes herzelieb in großes herzeleid wirt verwandelt, wer kan des balde vergessen? Böse leute tun das selbe; gute freunde stete gedenken an einander. Ferre wege, lange jar scheiden nicht geliebe. Ist sie mir leiblichen tot, in meiner gedechtnüß lebet sie mir doch immer. Herre Tod, ir müsset treulicher raten, sol eur rat icht nutzes bringen, anders, ir fledermaus, müsset als vor der vogel feindschaft tragen!

DER TOD

Das XXIIII. capitel

Lieb nicht alzu lieb, leid nicht alzu leid sol umb gewin und umb verlust bei weisem manne wesen. Des tustu nicht. Wer umb rat bittet und rates nicht folgen wil, dem ist auch nicht zu raten. Unser gütlicher rat kan an dir nicht geschaffen. Es sei dir nu lieb oder leid, wir wellen dir die warheit an die sunnen legen, es höre, wer da welle. Dein kurze vernunft, dein abgesniten sin, dein holes herze wellen aus leuten mer machen, dann sie gewesen mügen. Du machest aus einem menschen, was du wilt, es mag nicht mer gesein, dann als vil wir dir sagen wellen mit urlaub aller reinen frauen. Ein mensche wirt in sünden empfangen, mit unreinem, ungenan-

loved. Who can soon forget it when the heart's love
is turned into a great heart-ache? Wicked people
may do so, but dear friends think always of each
other. Long roads and many years divide not love.
Though she is dead to me in the body, yet she still
lives on in my memory. Death, you must advise
more sincerely if your advice is to be of any use.
Otherwise, bat that you are, you must still endure
the enmity of the birds.

DEATH

Chapter Twenty-four

Love not too dearly, grieve not too bitterly—that
should be the wise man's rule in gain and loss. You
do not act so. Whoever asks for advice and will not
take it, cannot be advised. Our well-meant advice
will not serve you. Whether you like it or not, we
will show you the truth in the broad light of day,
and let listen who will. You, with your limited intel-
ligence, your cropped comprehension, your hollow
heart, want to make men more than they can be.
Whatever you make of man, he can never be more
than what, by the ladies' leave, I will now tell you.
A man is conceived in sin, nourished in his mother's
body on unclean, indescribable filth, and born na-

tem unflat in müterlichem leibe generet, nacket geboren und ist ein besmireter binstock, ein ganzer
unlust, ein kotfaß, ein wurmspeise, ein stankhaus, ein
unlustiger spülzuber, ein faules as, ein schimelkaste,
en bodenloser sack, ein locherte tasche, ein blase-
balk, ein geitiger slund, ein stinkender leimtigel,
ein übelriechender harmkrug, ein übelsmekkender
eimer, ein betriegender tockenschein, ein leimen
raubhaus, ein unsetig leschtrog und ein gemalte be-
grebnüß. Es merke, wer da welle: ein jegliches ganz
gewurktes mensche hat neun löcher in seinem leibe,
aus den allen fleußet so unlustiger und unreiner unflat, das nicht unreiners gewesen mag. So schönes
mensche gesahestu nie, hettestu eines linzen augen
unde kündest es inwendig durchsehen, dir würde
darab grauen. Benim und zeuch ab der schönsten
frauen des sneiders farbe, so sihestu ein schemliche
tocken, ein schiere swelkende blumen von kurze
taurendem scheine und einen balde faulenden er-
denknollen. Weise uns ein handvol schöne aller
schönen frauen, die vor hundert jaren haben gelebt,
ausgenomen der gemalten an der wende, und habe
dir des keisers krone zu eigen! Laß hin fließen lieb,
laß hin fließen leid! Laß rinnen den Rein als ander
wasser! Eseldorf! weiser götling!

ked; he is a smeary bee-hive, a piece of loathsomeness, a barrel of muck, food for worms, a privy, a disgusting slop-pail, a rotting carcase, a moldy box, a bottomless bag, a torn placket, a bellows, a greedy gullet, a stinking glue-pot, an evil-smelling piss pot, a malodorous bucket, a deceitful puppet, a den of clay, an insatiable quenching tub, and a whited sepulcher. Let him hear who will: every normally made human being has nine holes in his body, and out of all of them comes loathsome and unclean filth than which nothing can be more foul. However beautiful a man might seem to you, if you had lynx eyes and could see within him, you would be horror-struck. If you take away from the loveliest woman the tailor's colors, you see a wretched doll, a swiftly wilting flower of brief splendor, a clod of earth that soon crumbles away. Show us a handful of beauty from all the lovely women who lived a hundred years ago, other than the painted ones on the wall, and the emperor's crown shall be yours. Let love and sorrow run their course! Let the Rhine flow on like other waters! O you clever, asinine dolt!

DER ACKERMAN

Das XXV. capitel

Pfei euch, böser schandensack! Wie vernichtet, übelhandelt und uneret ir den werden menschen, Gotes aller liebste creatüre, damit ir auch die gotheit swechet! Aller erste prüfe ich, das ir lügenhaftig seit und in dem paradise nicht getirmet, als ir sprechet. Weret ir in dem paradise gefallen, so westet ir, das Got den menschen und alle ding geschaffen hat, sie alle zumale gut beschaffen hat und den menschen über sie alle gesetzet, im ir aller herschaft befolhen und sie seiner füßen undertenig gemachet hat, also das der mensche den tieren des erdreichs, den vogeln des himels, den fischen des meres und allen früchten der erden herschen solte, als er auch tut. Solte dann der mensche so snöde, böse und unrein sein, als ir sprechet, werlich so hette Got gar unreinlichen und gar unnützlichen gewürket. Solte Gotes almechtige und wirdige hand so ein unreines und unfletiges menschwerk haben gewürket, als ir schreibet, streflicher und gemeilter würker were er. So stünde auch das nicht, das Got alle ding und den menschen über sie alle zumale gut hette beschaffen. Herre Tod, lasset eur unnütz klaffen! Ir schendet Gotes aller hübschestes werk. Engel, teufel, schret-

THE PLOWMAN

Chapter Twenty-five

Shame on you, you wicked slanderer! How you ill-treat, dishonor and destroy noble man, God's dearest creation, and thereby degrade the Godhead itself. Now I see you in your true colors for the first time, and know that you are a liar, and were not created in Paradise as you said. If you had been born in Paradise, you would know that God created man and all things, made them all well and set man over them all, and gave him dominion over them and put them under his feet, so that man should rule, as he does, over the beasts of the field and the fowl of the air, the fish of the sea and all the fruits of the earth. Were man as bad, wicked and unclean as you say, then indeed were God's work unclean and useless. If God's almighty and worthy hand had made man as unclean and foul as you describe him, He would be a bad and culpable creator. Then it would not be written that God made all things well, and man above all. Death, sir, cease your useless railing! You slander God's finest work. Angels, devils, goblins, screech owls, are all spirits within God's power; man is God's most noble piece of work, the most ingenious and the most free. God has made him in His

lein, klagemuter, das sint geiste in Gotes twange wesend; der mensche ist das aller achtberest, das aller behendest und das aller freiest Gotes werkstück. Im selber gleiche hat in Got gebildet, als er auch selbes in dem ersten urkunde der werlte hat gesprochen. Wo hat je werkman gewürket so behendes und reiches werkstück, einen so werkberlichen kleinen kloß als eines menschen haubet? In dem ist künstereiche kunst, allen Gote ebenteur, verborgen. Da ist in des augen apfel das gesichte, das aller gewissest zeuge, meisterlich in spiegels weise verwürket; bis an des himels klare zirkel würket es. Da ist in den oren das ferre würkende gehören, gar durchnechtiglichen mit einem dünnen felle vergitert, zu prüfung und merkung underscheid mancherlei süßes gedönes. Da ist in der nasen der ruch, durch zwei löcher ein und aus geend, gar sinniglichen verzimmert zu behegelicher senftigkeit alles lustsames und wünnesames riechens, das da ist nar der sele. Da sint in dem munde zene, alles leibfuters tegeliches malende einsacker; darzu der zungen dünnes blat, den leuten zu wissen bringend ganz der leute meinung; auch ist da des smackes allerlei koste lustsame prüfung. Dabei sint in dem kopfe aus herzen grunde geende sinne, mit den ein mensche, wie ferre er wil, gar snelle reichet; in die gotheit und darüber gar klimmet der mensche mit den sinnen. Allein der mensche ist empfahend der vernunft, des edelen hortes. Er ist allein der lieblich kloß, dem gleiche niemand dann Got gewürken kan, darin also

own image, as He Himself said at the world's first creation. Did ever a workman make so clever and rich a piece of work, so artful a little globe, as a human head? Hidden within it are ingenious arts of which God alone is capable. In the eyeball there is sight, the most trustworthy tool, made like a mirror with a masterly hand; it reaches to the clear ring of heaven. In the ears there is hearing that reaches out to the far distance; quite perfectly enclosed by a thin membrane it can search out and distinguish many a delightful sound. In the nose there is the sense of smell, that goes in and out through two openings, that is skilfully equipped for the easy acceptance of all pleasurable and delightful perfumes which are the nourishment of the soul. In the mouth there are the teeth that day after day grind and pack in the body's food, and as well the tongue's thin leaf that gives people full knowledge of people's meaning; and there too is taste agreeably testing out every kind of food. In the head moreover are thoughts from the depth of the heart, thoughts by which man reaches as far as he wishes. With his thoughts man climbs up to the Godhead and even beyond. Man alone possesses reason, that noble treasure. He alone is that dear clay which none but God can make, in which such skilful works are made, with all the mastery and wisdom of art. Let be, Death! You are man's foe and therefore have nothing good to say of him.

behende werk mit aller künste meisterschaft und weisheit sint gewürket. Lat faren, herre Tod! Ir seit des menschen feind; darumb ir kein gutes von im sprechet!

DER TOD

Das XXVI. capitel

Schelten, fluchen, wünschen, wie vil der ist, künnen keinen sack, wie kleine der ist, gefüllen; darzu: wider vil redende leute ist nicht zu kriegen mit worten. Es ge nur vür sich mitt deiner meinung, das ein mensche aller künste, hübscheit und wirdigkeit vol sei, dannoch muß es in unser netze fallen, mit unserem garne muß es gezücket werden. Gramatica, grundfeste aller guten rede, hilfet da nicht mit iren scharfen und wol gegerbten worten. Rhetorica, blüender grund der liebkosung, hilfet da nicht mir iren blüenden und reine geferbten reden. Loica, der warheit und unwarheit vürsichtige entscheiderin, hilfet da nicht mit irem verdackten verslahen, mit der warheit verleitung und krümmerei. Geometria, der erden prüferin, schetzerin und messerin, hilfet da nicht mit irer unfelender maße, mit iren rechten abgewichten. Arismetrica, der zale behende ausrichterin, hilfet da nicht mit irer rechnung, mit irer reitung mit iren behenden ziffern. Astronomia, des ge-

DEATH

Chapter Twenty-six

No amount of chiding, cursing and wishing will fill a sack, no matter how small it is. Besides, wordy people are not to be fought with words. Be it as it may, your view that man is full of every art, beauty and virtue, all the same he must fall into our net, must be caught by our snare. Grammar, the foundation of all good language, will not help with its sharp and well-trimmed words. Rhetoric, the flowering meadow of fair speech, will not help with its blossoms of brightly colored discourse. Logic, distinguishing subtly between truth and untruth, will not help with its veiled interpretations, with its misleading twists and turns of the truth. Geometry that tests, estimates and surveys the earth will not help with its infallible measurement, its accurate weighing. Arithmetic, skilfully marshalling digits, will not help with its reckoning, its counting, its ingenious numbers. Astronomy, the mistress of the heavenly bodies, will not help with its powers of the stars, its

stirnes meisterin, hilfet da nicht mit irem sterngewalte, mit einflusse der planeten. Musica, des gesanges und der stimme geordente handreicherin, hilfet da nicht mit iren süßen gedöne, mit iren feinen stimmen. Philozophia, acker der weisheit, zwirund in natürlicher erkantnüß und in guter siten würkung geackert und geset und volkomenlich gewachsen; Physica mit iren mancherlei steurenden trenken; Geomancia, mit satzung der planeten und des himelsreifes zeichen auf erden allerlei frage behende verantwürterin; Piromancia, sleunige und warhaftige warsagens aus feur würkerin; Idromancia, in wassers gewürke der zukünftigkeit entwerferin; Astroloia mit oberlendischer sachen macht irdisches laufes auslegerin; Ciromancia, nach henden und nach des teners kreisen hübsche warsagerin; Nigromancia, mit totenopfer, fingerlein und mit sigel der geiste gewaltige twingerin; Alchimia mit der metalle seltsamer verwandelung; Notoria, die kunst mit iren süßen gebeten, mit irem starken besweren; Augurium, der vogelkose vernemer und daraus zukünftiger sachen warhafter zusager; Aruspicium, nach alteropfers rauche witze kund tuende ausrichtung; Pedomancia mit kinder gedirme und Ornomancia mit aurhanen dermen lüplerin; Iura, wandelberes und widersprüchiges recht, und Iuriste, der gewissenlos criste, mit rechtes und unrechtes vürsprechung, mit seinen krummen articlen — die und ander, den vorgeschriben anhangende künste helfen

influence of the planets. Music, the harmonious handmaid of song and the voice, will not help with its sweet sounds and its lovely voices. Philosophy, the field of wisdom, doubly plowed and sown and well planted with the knowledge of nature and the effect of true morality; physic with its many kinds of fortifying drafts; geomancy which, from the position of the planets and the signs of the zodiac, astutely answers many an earthly question; pyromancy that can prophesy swiftly and truly from fire; hydromancy that can see the future in the ways of water; astrology that can interpret events on earth through the influence of other worlds; chiromancy, the beautiful soothsayer from the lines of the hand; necromancy that can raise spirits by means of sacrifices to the dead, rings and symbols; alchemy with its strange transmutation of metals; conjuration with its sweet prayers and powerful invocations; augury that knows the language of birds and therefore truthfully foretells things to come; haruspicy, the prediction of the future from the smoke of the burnt sacrifice; pedomancy and ornomancy that perform magic with the entrails of children and blackcocks; jurisprudence, the changeable and contradictory law, and the jurist, the conscienceless Christian, with his distortions of right and wrong, with his crooked clauses —all these and other kindred arts are of no help whatever. Every man must always be brought low by us, must be fulled in our fulling trough and

zumale nicht. Jedes mensche mußje von uns umbge-
stürzet, in unserem walktroge gewalken und in unserem rollfasse gefeget werden. Das glaube, du
üppiger geuknecht!

DER ACKERMAN

Das XXVII. capitel

Man sol nicht übel mit übel rechen; gedultig sol ein
man wesen, gebeitend der tugend lere. Den pfad wil
ich nach treten, of ir leichte noch nach ungedult
gedultig werdet. Ich vernim an eurer rede, ir meinet, ir ratet mir gar treulich. Wonet treue bei euch,
so ratet mir mit treuen in gesworenes eides weise.
In was wesens sol ich nu mein leben richten? Ich
bin vormals in der lieben lustigen e gewesen; warzu
sol ich mich nu wenden? In werltlich oder in geist-
lich ordenung? Die sint mir beide offen. Ich nam
vür mich in den sin allerlei leute wesen, schatzte
und wug sie mit fleiße: unvolkomen, brüchig und
etwe vil mit sünden fand ich sie alle. In zweifel bin
ich, wo ich hin keren sülle; mit gebrechen ist bekümmert aller leute anstal. Herre Tod, ratet! Rates
ist not! In meinem sinne finde, wene und glaube ich
vü war, das nie so reines, götliches nest und wesen
kume nimmermer. Bei der sele, ich spriche: Weste
ich, das mir in der e gelingen solte als e, in der e

cleansed in our scouring drum. Make up your mind to that, you conceited clod-hopper!

THE PLOWMAN

Chapter Twenty-seven

One should not return evil for evil; a man should be patient and follow the teachings of virtue. That path I mean to follow, in case you should perhaps become patient after your impatience. I gather from your speech that you think you have advised me most sincerely. If there be any truth in you, then advise me in good faith as if you did so upon oath. On what basis should I now order my life? Formerly I lived in the sweet and pleasant state of matrimony; which way should I now turn? To the secular or the spiritual estate? Both are open to me. I have imagined the existence of all kinds of people; carefully I weighed them up and considered them; but all seemed to me imperfect, frail and somehow sinful. I am in doubt which way I should turn; every human condition is afflicted with some fault. Advise me, Death! I have need of advice. I truly think, consider and believe that so pure and godly a nest and life will never come again. I declare upon my soul

wolte ich leben, die weile lebend were mein leben. Wünnesam, lustsam, fro und wolgemut ist ein man, der ein biderb weib hat, er wandere, wo er wander. Einem jeden solchen man ist auch lieb, nach narung zu stellen und zu trachten. Im ist auch lieb, ere mit eren, treue mit treuen, güte mit güte widergelten. Er bedarf ir nicht hüten; wan sie ist die beste hut, die ir ein frumes weib selber tut. Wer seinem weibe nicht glauben und trauen wil, der muß stecken in steten sorgen. Herre von oberlanden, fürste von vil selden, wol im, wen du so mit reinem bettegenossen begabest! Er sol den himel ansehen, dir mit aufgerackten henden danken alle tage. Tut das beste, herre Tod, vil vermügender herre!

DER TOD

Das XXVIII. capitel

Loben one ende, schenden one zil, was sie vürfassen, pflegen etelich leute. Bei loben und bei schenden sol fuge und maße sein; ob man ir eines bedürfe, das man sein stat habe. Du lobest sunder maße eliches leben; jedoch wellen wir dir sagen von elichem leben, ungerüret aller reinen frauen. Als balde ein man ein weib nimt, als balde ist er selbander in unserer gefengnüß. Zuhand hat er einen handslag,

that if I knew that I would be as lucky in matrimony as I was before, then I would live married as long as my life lasts. A man who has a good wife is enraptured, merry, gay and in good spirits wherever he may go. Such a man is glad to strive and struggle for food. He is glad also to return honor for honor, faith for faith, good for good. He does not need to guard her, for an honest woman is her own best guardian. A man who will not trust and believe his own wife, is sunk in constant care. Lord of the high places, prince of many mansions, fortunate is the man to whom You give so pure a bedfellow. He should fix his eyes upon heaven and with hands upraised thank You every day of his life. Do your best, Death, you who are so powerful a master.

DEATH

Chapter Twenty-eight

Whatever they undertake, some people have a habit of praising without end, of vilifying without purpose. There should be some bound and measure in praise and vilification, so that they can be properly used when needed. You praise married life out of all measure; however, we will tell you something about married life, all pure wives notwithstanding. As soon as a man has taken a wife, they are both our

einen anhang, einen handsliten, ein joch, ein kumat,
ein bürde, einen sweren last, eine fegeteufel, ein
telegliche rosfeilen, der er mit nichte nicht enberen
mag, die weile wir mit im nicht tun unser genade.
Ein beweibter man hat doner, schaur, füchse, slan-
gen alle tage in seinem hause. Ein weib stellet alle
tage darnach, das sie man werde. Zeuchet er auf, so
zeuchet sie nider; wil er so, so wil sie sust; wil er
dahin, so wie sie dorthin. Solches spiles wirt er sat
und sigelos alle tage. Triegen, listen, smeichen, spin-
nen, liebkosen, widerburren, lachen, weinen kan sie
wol in einem augenblicke; angeboren ist es sie. Siech
zu arbeit, gesund zu wollust, darzu zam und wilde ist
sie, wann sie des bedarf. Umb werwort finden bedarf sie keines ratmannes. Geboten ding nicht tun,
verboten ding tun fleißet sie sich alzeit. Das ist ir
zu süße, dast ist ir zu saur; des ist ir zu vil, des ist ir
zu wenig; nu ist es zu fru, nu ist es zu spate; also
wirt es alles gestrafet. Wirt dann icht von ir gelobet,
das muß mit schanden in einem drechselstule gedret
werden; dannoch wirt das loben dicke mit gespötte
gemischet. Ein man, der in der e lebet, kan kein
mittel aufhaben. Ist er zu gütig, ist er zu scharf, an
in beiden wirt er mit schaden gestrafet. Er sei nur
halb gütig-scharf, dannoch ist da kein mittel; sched-
lich oder streflich wirt es je. Alle tage neue anmu-
tung oder keifen, alle wochen fremde aufsatzung
oder murmeln, alle monat neuen unlustigen unflat
oder grauen, alle jar neues kleiden oder tegeliches
strafen muß ein beweibeter man haben, er gewinne

prisoners. He has a binding duty, a care, a hand sledge, a yoke, a horse-collar, a burden, a heavy load, a demon, a daily horse rasp, which he cannot get rid of until we show our mercy toward him. A married man has thunder, hail, foxes and serpents in his house every day. A wife is always scheming to make herself the master. If he pulls upward, she pulls downward; if he wants this, she wants that, if he wants to go this way, she wants to go that. Every day he has more than enough of that game, a game he can't win. Deceiving, cheating, flattering, wheedling, petting, opposing, laughing, crying—she can do all that at once: it's born in her. She's ill when there's work, well when there's pleasure, and she's tame or wild, just as she needs. She needs no adviser to find excuses. She's always busy not doing the things she ought to do and doing those she ought not to do. She complains about everything: this is too sweet, that is too sour; this is too much, that is too little; first it's too early, then it's too late. If for once she praises something, it's a shame how it has to be turned this way and that as on a lathe, and even then the praise is often mixed with mockery. For a married man there is no golden mean. Whether he is too kind or too strict, he gets blamed and berated for both. Let him be half kind and half strict, still that is no means to avoid berating and blaming. For a married man, no matter whom he takes to wife, every day brings a new exaction or a row, every week strange demands or grumbling, every

es, wo er welle. Der nacht gebrechen sei aller vergessen; von alters wegen schemen wir uns. Schonten wir nicht der biderben frauen, von den unbiderben künden wir vil mer singer und sagen. Wisse, was du lobest; du kennest nicht gold bei bleie!

DER ACKERMAN

Das XXVIIII. capitel

Frauen schender müssen geschendet werden, sprechen der warheit meister. Wie geschicht euch dann, herre Tod? Eur unvernünftiges frauen schenden, wie wol es mit frauen urlaub ist, ist werlich euch schendlich und den frauen schemlich. In maniges weisen meisters geschrifte findet man, das one weibes steure niemand mag mit selden gesteuret werden; wan weibes und kinder habe ist nicht das minste teil der irdischen selden. Mit solcher warheit hat sein trostbuch ein Römer Boecius hin geleget. Philozophia, die weise meisterin, und jeder abenteurlicher und sinniger man ist mir des zeuge: kein mannes zucht kan wesen, sie sei dann gemeistert mit frauen züchte. Es sage, wer es welle: ein züchtiges, schönes, keusches und an eren unverrucktes weib ist vor aller irdischer eugelweide. So menlichen man gesach ich nie, der rechte mutig wurde, er würde

month disgusting filth or anger, every year new dresses or wrangling day in day out. We say nothing about goings-on at night; at our age we are ashamed. But for sparing respectable women, we could sing a much longer song about unrespectable ones. Know what you are praising: you can't tell gold from lead.

THE PLOWMAN

Chapter Twenty-nine

Those who slander women shall themselves be slandered, the sages say. So what is to be done with you, Death? Your unreasonable slandering of women, even though by the ladies' leave, in fact disgraces you and shames women. In the writings of many a wise teacher it is said that without a woman's guiding hand no-one can steer his way to good fortune, for the possession of wife and children is not the least part of earthly happiness. Such was the truth presented by Boetius the famous Roman, in his book of consolation. I call to witness philosophy, our wise teacher, and every outstanding and thoughtful man, for this: there can be no manly virtue except subject to virtuous women. They may say what they like— a virtuous, beautiful and chaste wife, with her honor untarnished, is above all other earthly delights. I never saw any man, however valiant, come to

dann mit frauen troste gesteuret. Wo der guten sa-
menung ist, da sihet man es alle tage; auf allen pla-
nen, auf allen hofen, in allen turnieren, in allen her-
ferten tun die frauen je das beste. Wer in frauen
dienste ist, der muß sich aller missetat anen. Rechte
zucht und ere leren die werden frauen in irer schule.
Irdischer freuden sint gewaltig die frauen; sie schaffen, das in zu eren geschicht alle hübscheit und
kurzweil auf erden. Einer reinen frauen fingerdroen
strafet und züchtiget vür alle waffen einen frumen
man. One liebkosen mit kurzer rede: aller werlte
aufhaltung, festung under merung sint die werden
frauen. Jedoch bei golde blei, bei weize raden, bei
allerlei münze beislege und bei weibe unweib müssen wesen; dannoch die guten sullen der bösen
nicht engelten. Das glaubet, haubetman von kriege!

DER TOD

Das XXX. capitel

Einen kolben vür einen kloß goles, eine köten vüur
einen topasion, einen kisling vür einen rubin nimt
ein narre; die heuscheur eine burg, die Tunau das
mer, de meusar einen falken nennet der tore. Also
lobestu der augen lust, der ursachen schetzestu
nicht; wan du weist nicht, das alles, das in der

achievement except with a woman's help and guidance. One sees it every day, wherever there is good company, in all places, at all courts, at all tourneys, on all campaigns, it is the women who do the greatest things. He who is in the service of women must shun any evil deed. Noble women teach dignity and honor in their school. Women command earthly joys; it is in their honor that all feasts and festivities are held. The threat of a virtuous woman's finger does more than any weapon to punish and discipline a brave man. In brief, and flattery aside, noble women are the preservation, defence and increase of all mankind. However, along with gold there has to be lead, thistles along with wheat, false coin with good and shrews as well as women. All the same, the good should not have to pay for the bad. Take that from me, captain of conflicts!

DEATH

Chapter Thirty

An ignorant man mistakes a chunk of ore for a nugget, a knuckle-bone for a topaz, a pebble for a ruby; a fool calls a haystack a castle, the Danube the sea and a buzzard a falcon. In the same way you praise the pleasure of the eye without taking causes into account. For you do not know that everything in the

werlte ist, ist eintweder begerung des fleisches oder
begerung der augen oder höhe des lebens. Die begerung des fleisches zu wollust, die begerung der
augen zu gute, die höhe des lebens zu ere sint geneiget. Das gut bringet girung und geitigkeit, die
wollust machet geilheit und unkeuscheit, die ere
bringet hochfart und rum. Von gute türstigkeit und
forchte, von wollust bosheit und sünde, von ere guft
und eitelkeit müssen je komen. Kündestu das vernemen, du würdest eitelkeit in aller werlte finden;
und geschehe dir dann liebe oder leide, das würdestu dann gütlichen leiden, auch uns ungestrafet
lassen. Aber als vil als ein esel leiren kan, als vil
kanstu die warheit vernemen. Darumb so sein wir
so sere mit dir bekümmert. Do wir Pyramum den
jüngeling mit Tisben der meide, die beide ein sele
und willen hetten, schieden, do wir künig Alexan-
drum aller werlte herschaft entenigten, do wir Paris
von Troja und Helenam von Kriechen zerstorten, do
wurden wir nicht also sere als von dir gestrafet.
Umb keiser Karel, markgraven Wilhelm, Dietrich
von Berne, den starken Boppen und umb den hür-
nen Seifrid haben wir nicht so vil müe gehabet.
Aristotilem und Avicennam klagen noch heute vil
leute, dannoch sein wir ungemüet. Do David der
gedultig und Salomon, der weisheit schrein, sturben,
do ward uns mer gedanket dann gefluchet. Die vor
waren, die sint alle dahin; du und alle, die nu sint
oder noch werden, müssen alle hinnach. Dannoch
beleiben wir Tod hie herre!

world is either the lust of the flesh or lust of the eye or pride of life. The lust of the flush seeks voluptuousness, the lust of the eye seeks possession and the pride of life seeks honor. Possession brings covetousness and avarice; voluptuousness brings lechery and unchastity, honor brings arrogance and vainglory. From possession come always swaggering and fear, from voluptuousness come wickedness and sin, from honor, pride and vanity. If you could grasp that, you would find vanity everywhere, and whether you suffered joy or sorrow, you would bear it with temperance and would not chide us. But you can no more learn to grasp the truth than an ass can learn to play the lyre. And that is why you are so much trouble to us. When we parted the boy Pyramus and the girl Thisbe, who were united in heart and soul, when we deprived King Alexander of the mastery of the whole world, when we destroyed Paris of Troy and Helen of Greece, we were not so chidden as we are now by you. We did not have so much trouble on account of Charlemagne, the Margrave Wilhelm, Dietrich von Bern, Boppe the Strong, and the invulnerable Siegfried. Many people still lament Aristotle and Avicenna, yet they leave us unmolested. When King David died, who was slow to anger, and King Solomon, the ark of wisdom, we were more thanked than cursed. Those who came before are all dead and gone, and you and all who now are or shall be, must all follow. We, Death, remain still the master here.

DER ACKERMAN

Das XXXI. capitel

Eigene rede verteilet dicke einen man und gerlich einen, der jetzund eines und darnach ein anderes redet. Ir habet vor gesprochen, ir seit etwas und doch nicht ein geist und seit des lebens ende und euch sein alle irdische land empfolhen. So sprechet ir nu, wir müssen alle dahin, und ir Tod beleibet hie herre. Zwo widerwertig rede mügen mit einander nicht war gewesen. Sullen wir von leben alle dahin secheiden und irdisch leben sol alles ende haben und ir seit, als ir sprechet, des lebens ende, so merke ich: wann nimmer lebens ist, so wirt nimmer sterbens und todes. Wo komt ir dann hin, herre Tod? In himel müget ir nicht wonen, der ist gegeben allein den guten geisten. Kein geist seit ir nach eurer rede. Wann ir dann auf erden nimmer zu schaffen habet und die erde nimmer weret, so müsset ir gerichtes in die helle; darinnen müsset ir one ende krochen. Da werden auch die lebendigen und die toten an euch gerochen. Nach eurer wechselrede kan sich niemand gerichten. Solten alle irdische ding so böse, snöde und untüchtig sein, als ir sprechet, so müsten sie von Gote untüchtig sein beschaffen und gewürket. Des ist er von anfang der werlte nie ge-

THE PLOWMAN

Chapter Thirty-one

A man is often condemned out of his own mouth, especially if he says first one thing and then another. You said previously that you were something, yet not a spirit, that you were the end of life and that all the lands of the world were confided to you. Now you say we must all go hence and you, Death, remain master here. Two contradictory statements cannot both be true. If we are all to depart from life and if all life on earth is to have an end, and if you, as you say, are the end of life, then I infer that once there is no more life there will be no more dying and no more death. What becomes of you then, Death? You cannot be in Heaven, for that is given over to the good spirits only. But according to what you said, you are not a spirit. If you have nothing left to do on earth, and the earth is no longer there, then you must go straight to hell. And there you must groan for ever. There the living and the dead will be avenged upon you. No-one can make head or tail of your contradictory talk. If all earthly things are as wicked, bad and useless as you say, God's works must have been created useless. He has never been accused of that since the beginning of the world.

zigen. Tugend lieb gehabet, bosheit gehasset, sünde übersehen und gerochen hat Got unz her. Ich glaube, hinnach tue er auch das selbe. Ich han von jugend auf gehöret lesen und gelernet, wie Got alle ding gut beschaffen habe. Ir sprechet, wie alle irdische leben und wesen sullen ende nemen; so sprichet Plato und ander weissagen, das in allen sachen eines zerüttung des andern berung sei und wie alle sache auf urkunde sein gebauret und wie des himels lauf, aller planeten und der erden von einem in das ander verwandelt werde und ewig sei. Mit eurer wankelrede, darauf niemand bauen sol, wellet ir mich von meiner klage schrecken. Des berufe ich mich mit euch an Got, meinen heiland, herre Tod, mein verderber! Damit gebe euch Got ein böses amen!

DER TOD

Das XXXII. capitel

Oft ein man, wann et der anhebet zu reden, im werde dann understoßen, nicht aufgehören kan. Du bist auch aus dem selben stempfel gewürket. Wir haben gesprochen und sprechen noch, damit wellen wir ende machen: die erde und alle ir behaltung ist auf unstetigkeit gebauet. In diser zeit ist sie wandelber worden, wan alle ding haben sich verkeret, das

God has so far loved virtue, hated wickedness and pardoned or avenged sin. I believe He will do the same henceforth. From my boyhood I have heard, read and learned that God created all things well. You say that all earthly life and creation must have an end. But Plato and other philosophers say that the destruction of one thing is the birth of another, that all things are built upon creation, and that the course of the heavens, of all planets and of the world is a transformation of one into another and is eternal. You want to deter me from my complaint by your ambiguous talk on which no-one can rely. Therefore I appeal to God, my savior, against you, Death, my destroyer. May God give you a bad amen!

DEATH

Chapter Thirty-two

Often when a man has begun to talk he cannot stop, unless he is interrupted. You are one of that stamp. We have said before, and we say it again once and for all: the earth and all that therein is are built upon transience. In our day they have become unsettled, for all things have been reversed, the last has become the first, the first has become the last,

hinder hervür, das voder hinhinder, das under gen berge, das oben gen tale. Das ebich an das rechte hat die meist menige volkes gekeret. Zu feures flammen stetigkeit kan icht alles menschliches geslechte getreffen; einen schein zu greifen, einen guten, treuen, beistendigen freund zu finden, ist nahend gleich mügelich auf erden worden. Alle menschen sint mer zu bosheit dann zu güte geneiget. Tut nu jemand icht gutes, das tut er uns besorgend. Alle leute mit allem irem gewürke sint vol eitelkeit worden. Ir leib, ir weib, ir kinder, ir ere, ir gut und alles ir vermügen fleuchet alles dahin, mit einem augenblicke verswindet es, mit dem winde verwischet es, noch kan der schein noch der schate nicht beleiben. Merke, prüfe, sich und schaue, was nu der menschen kinder auf erden haben, wie sie berg und tal, stock und stein, aue und gefilde, der Alpen wildnüß, des meres grund, der erden tiefe durch irdisches gutes willen durchgründen in regen, winden, doner, schaur, sne und in allerlei ungewiter, wie sie slechte, stollen und tiefe fundgruben in die erden durchgraben der erden adern durchhauen glanzerze suchend, die sie durch seltsenkeit willen vür alle ding lieb haben, wie sie holz wellen, gewand zeuen, heuser den swalben gleiche klecken, pflanzen und pelzen baumgarten, ackern das erdreich, bauen weinwachs, machen mülwerk, zünden zinsel, bestellen fischerei, weidwerk und wildwerk, große herte vihes zusamen treiben, vil knechte und meide haben, hohe pferd reiten, goldes, silbers, edel gesteines,

what was below has risen above and what was above has fallen below. The greater part of people has turned wrong into right. The whole human race is as stable as the fire's flame, and to find a good, loyal, helping friend on earth is about as possible as to grasp a beam of light. All men are more inclined to evil than to good. Should someone do good, he does it from fear of us. In all their doings all men have become nothing but vanity. Everything passes away, their body, their wife, their children, their honor, their possessions and all their power vanish away in the twinkling of an eye, are gone with the wind, not a semblance nor a shadow can remain. Mark and examine, look and see what the sons of men do upon earth, how for the sake of earthly goods they explore in rain and wind, thunder, hail, snow and other inclement weather the mountains and valleys, stocks and stones, meadows and fields, the alpine wilderness, the bottom of the sea and the bowels of the earth, how they dig pits and tunnels and deep shafts into the earth, how they drive through the veins of the earth in their search for glittering metals, which for their rarity they love above all else, how they hew wood, weave garments, plaster houses like the swallows, plant and graft orchards, plow the soil, lay out vineyards, make mills, light fires, go fishing and hunting, raise great herds of cattle, have many men and maid servants, ride high upon a horse, have houses and chests full of gold, silver, precious stones and sumptuous garments and all kinds of other pos-

reiches gewandes und allerlei ander habe heuser
und kisten vol haben, wollust und wünnen pflegen,
darnach sie tag und nacht stellen und trachten. Was
ist das alles? Das alles ist eitelkeit über eitelkeit und
beswerung der sele, vergenglich et als der gesterig
tag, der vergangen ist. Mit kriege und mit raube
gewinnen sie es; wan je mer gehabet, je mer gerau-
bet. Zu kriegen und zu werren lassen sie es nach in.
O die tötliche menscheit ist stete .in engsten, in
trübsal, in leide, in besorgen, in forchten, in scheu-
hung, in wetagen, in siechtagen, in trauren, in betrübnüß, in jamer, in kummer und in mancherlei widerwertigkeit; und je mer ein man irdisches gutes
hat, je mer im widerwertigkeit begegent. Noch ist
das das aller gröste, das ein mensche nicht gewissen
kan, wann, wo oder wie wir über es urplüpfling fallen und es jagen, zu laufen den weg der tötlichen.
Die bürde müssen tragen herren und knechte, man
und weib, reich und arm, gut und böse. O leidige
zuversicht, wie wenig achten dein die tummen!
Wann es zu spate ist, so wellen sie alle frum werden. Darumb laß dein klagen, sun! Trit in welchen
orden du wilt, du findest gebrechen und eitelkeit
darinnen. Jedoch kere von dem bösen und tue das
gute; suche den fride und tue in stete; über alle irdische ding habe lieb rein und lauter gewissen! Und
das wir dir rechte geraten haben, des komen wir mit
dir an Got, den ewigen, den großen und den starken.

sessions, how they indulge in voluptuousness and pleasure, for which they strive and labor day and night. What is all this? It is nothing but vanity of vanities and vexation of spirit, fleeting as yesterday which has already passed. They gain it by war and robbery, for the more they have the more they rob. They bequeath it to war and strife. Oh, mortal man goes ever in dread, in tribulation and in sorrow, in care, fear, terror, pain, sickness, lamentation, affliction, suffering and woe and every kind of trouble, and the more earthly goods a man has, the more trouble he finds. The greatest of all is that a man cannot know when, where or how we shall, all of a sudden, fall upon him and chase him along the road of mortality. All must bear this burden, lords and servants, men and women, rich and poor, good and bad. O miserable prospect, how little the foolish heed you! When it is too late, they all want to be virtuous. So put an end to your lamentation, man! Go where you will, among the members of every estate you will find frailty and vanity. But shun evil and do good; seek peace and keep it. Above all earthly things cherish a clear conscience. And since we have counselled you wisely, we come with you before God, Who is eternal, great and strong.

GOT

Das XXXIII. capitel

Der lenze, der sumer, der herbest und der winter, die vier erquicker und handhaber des jares, die wurden zwifertig mit großen kriegen. Ir jeder rümte sich, und wolte jeglicher in seiner würkung der beste sein. Der lenze sprach, er erquickte und machte güftig alle früchte; der sumer sprach, er machte reif und zeitig alle früchte; der herbest sprach, er brechte und zechte ein beide in stedel, in keller und in die heuser alle früchte; der winter sprach, er verzerte und vernutzte alle früchte und vertribe alle gifttragende würme. Sie rümten sich und kriegeten faste; sie hetten aber vergessen, das sie sich gewaltiger herschaft rümten. Ebengleiche tut ir beide. Der klager klaget sein verlust, als ob sie sein erberecht were; er wenet nicht, das sie im von uns were verlihen. Der Tod rümet sich herschaft, die er doch allein von uns zu lehen hat empfangen. Der klaget, das nicht sein ist; diser rümet sich herschaft, die er nicht von im selber hat. Jedoch der krieg ist nicht gar one sache: ir habet beide wol gefochten. Den twinget leid zu klagen, disen die anfechtung des klagers, die warheit zu sagen. Darumb: klager, habe

GOD

Chapter Thirty-three

Spring, summer, autumn and winter, the four quick-
eners and upholders of the year fell into discord and
great disputation. Each of them boasted that he and
his works were the best of all. Spring said that he
brought all fruits to life and made them flourish;
summer said that he ripened all fruits to maturity;
autumn said that he brought all fruits into the
barns, cellars and houses; winter said that he con-
sumed and used up all fruits and drove away all poi-
sonous insects. So they boasted and argued violent-
ly. But they had forgotten that they were boasting
of a delegated power. You two do likewise. The
plaintiff complains about his loss, as though his inheritance were in question; he does not consider that
it was granted to him by Us. Death boasts about his
power which, however, he received in fief from Us
alone. The former sues for something that is not his,
the latter boasts of a power that is not his own.
Nevertheless the dispute is not quite without justi-
fication; you have both fought well. The one is
driven by sorrow to bring his complaint, the other
by the plaintiff's attack to state the truth. Therefore

ere, Tod, habe sige, seit jeder mensche das leben
dem Tode, den leib der erden, die sele uns pflichtig
ist zu geben.

IOHANNES M. A.

Immer wachender wachter aller werlte; got aller
göter; herre wunderhaftiger; herre aller herren; al-
mechtigster aller geiste; fürste aller fürstentume;
brunne, aus dem alle gutheit fleußet; heiliger aller
heiligen; kroner und die krone; loner und der lon;
kurfürste, in des küre sten alle küre; wol im ward,
wer manschaft von dir empfehet! Der engel freude
und wünne; eindruck der aller höchsten formen;
altgreiser jüngeling, erhöre mich!

O licht, das da nicht empfehet ander licht; licht,
das da verfinstert und verblendet alles auswendiges
licht; schein, vor dem verswindet aller ander schein;
schein, zu des achtung alle licht sint finsternüß;
licht, zu dem aller schein ein schate ist, dem alle
finsternüß licht sint, dem aller schate erscheinet;
licht, das in der beginstnüß gesprochen hat: werde
licht!; feur, das unverloschen alweg brinnet; anfang
und ende, erhöre mich!

I award honor to the plaintiff and victory to Death,
since every man is bound to give his life to Death,
his body to the earth and his soul to Me.

JOHANNES M.A.

J ust and vigilant guardian of all the world; God of
all gods; Lord of miracles; Lord of all lords; Almighty spirit above all spirits; prince over all prince-
doms; fountain whence all goodness flows; sanctifier
of all saints; crowner and crown; rewarder and reward; elective prince in whose election are all the
elect; fortunate is he who is Your vassal. Joy and
rapture of the angels; molder of all highest forms;
ancient of youthful days, hear me!

O light that admits of no other light; light that ob-
scures and darkens all outward light; brightness before which all other brightness fades away; brightness before which all lights are darkness; light before
which all brightness is shadow, through which all
darkness becomes light, through which all shadow
shines bright; light which said in the beginning, let
there be light! Unextinguished fire that burns for
ever; beginning and end, hear me!

Heil und selde über alles heil und selde; weg one allen irrsal zu dem ewigen leben; bestes, one das dann nicht bessers ist; leben, dem alle ding leben; warheit über alle warheit; weisheit, umbsließende alle weisheit; aller sterke gewaltiger; rechtes und gerechter hant beschaurer; widerbringer aller brüche; ganz vermügender in allen kreften; nothaft, zu dem alle gute ding als zu dem weisel der bin nehen und halten sich; ursache aller sache, erhöre mich!

Aller seuchten widerbringender arzet; meister aller meister; allein vater aller schepfung; alweg und an allen enden gegenwürtiger zuseher; aus der muter leibe in der erden gruft selbmügender geleiter; bilder aller formen; grundfeste aller guten werke; aller werlte warung; hasser aller unfletigkeit, loner aller guten dinge; allein rechter richter; einig, aus den anfange alle sache ewiglich nimmer weichen mag, erhöre mich!

Nothelfer in allen engsten; fester knode, den niemand aufbinden mag; volkomenes wesen, das aller volkomenheit mechtig ist; aller heimlicher und niemandes wissender sachen warhaftiger erkenner; ewiger freuden spender, irdischer wünner störer; wirt, ingesinde und hausgenosse aller guten leute; jeger, dem alle spor unverborgen sint; aller sinne

Hallowing and bliss above all hallowing and bliss; to life everlasting the way that strays not; best without which nothing can be better; life through which all things have life; truth above all truths; wisdom that contains all wisdoms; master of all might; keeper of right and justice; restorer of all wrongs; commander of all forces; surety to which all good things turn and cling like bees to the queen bee; first cause of all causes, hear me!

All-healing physician of all ills; master of masters; sole Father of all creation; watcher present at all times and in all places; all-sufficing guide from womb to earthly grave; former of all shapes; firm foundation of all good deeds; sustainer of the whole world; hater of all uncleanness; rewarder of all goodness; only just judge; tribune whose powers no suit ever escapes, hear me!

Need's helper in all sore straits; firm knot that none can unbind; perfect being who commands all perfection; true discoverer of all things secret and unknown; donor of joys everlasting, destroyer of earthly pleasures; host, staff and companion of all good people; huntsman from whom no track is hidden; fine mold of all the senses; just and coherent center

ein feiner einguß; rechter und zusamenhaltender mittel aller zirkelmaße; genediger erhörer aller zu dir rufender, erhöre mich!

Nahender beistendiger aller bedürftigen; traurenwender aller in dich hoffender; her hungerigen widerfüller, satung der durstigen, labung der kranken; sigel der aller höchsten majestat; besließung des himels armonei; einiger erkenner aller menschen gedanke; ungleicher bilder aller menschen antlitze; planete gewaltiger aller planeten; ganz würkender einfluß alles gestirnes; des himels hofes gewaltiger und wünnesamer hofemeister; twang, vor dem alle himelische ordenung aus irem geewigten angel nimmer treten mag; lichte sunne, erhöre mich!

Ewige lucerne; ewiges immerlicht; rechte farender marner, des kocke underget nimmer; banierfürer, under des banier niemand sigelos wirt; der helle abgrundes stifter; der erden kloßes bauer; des meres strames tremer; der luft unstetigkeit mischer; des feures hitze kreftiger; aller elemente tirmer; doners, blitzens, nebels, schaures, snees, regens, regenbogens, miltaues, windes, reifes und aller irer mitwürkung einiger essemeister; alles himelischen heres gewaltiger herzog; unversagenlicher keiser; aller senftiglichster aller sterkster, aller barmherzigster schepfer, erbarme dich mein und erhöre mich!

of all circles; You who listen in mercy to all who cry to You, hear me!

Neighbor who brings help to all in need; who turns away sadness from all who put their hope in You; who brings food to the hungry and drink to the thirsty; who soothes the sick; seal of majesty in the highest; keeper of the heavenly harmony; who alone knows all men's thoughts; sculptor of the manifold faces of man; mighty planet before all planets; omnipotent influence of all stars; strong master of delight in the courts of heaven; force that binds the heavenly orders in their eternal places, bright sun, hear me!

Eternal lantern, everlasting perpetual light; true helmsman whose ship never founders; standard-bearer under whose banner no-one goes defeated; establisher of hell's abyss; earth's edifier; who stirs the waves of the sea; who mingles the unstable airs; who fans the fire; creator of all the elements; sole master smith of thunder, lightning, mist, hail, snow, rain, rainbows, mildew, winds and hoar frost and all their works; commander-in-chief of the heavenly hosts; emperor to whom none can deny allegiance; most gentle, most strong, most merciful creator, have mercy upon me and hear me!

Schatz, von dem alle schetze entsprießen; ursprung, aus dem alle reine ausflüsse fließen; leiter, nach dem niemand irre wirt; aus nichte ichts, aus ichte nichts allen vermügender würker; aller weilwesen, zeitwesen und immerwesen ganz mechtiger erquicker, aufhalter und vernichter, des wesen joch, als du in dir selber bist, ausrichten, visieren, entwerfen und abnemen niemand kan; ganzes gut über alles gut; aller wirdigster ewiger herre Ihesu, empfahe genediglichen den geist, empfahe gütlichen die sele meiner aller liebsten frauen! Die ewigen rue gib ir, mit deiner genaden taue labe sie, under den schaten deiner flügel behalt sie! Nim sie, herre, in dein volkomen genüge, da genüget den minsten als den meisten! Laß sie, herre, von dannen sie komen ist, wonen in deinem reiche bei den ewen seligen geisten!

Mich reuet Margaretha, mein auserweltes weib. Günne ir, genadenreicher herre, in deiner almechtigen und ewigen gotheit spiegel sich ewiglichen ersehen, beschauen und erfreuen, darin sich alle engelische kore erleuchten!

Alles, das under des ewigen fanentragers fanen gehöret, es sei, welcherlei creatüre es sei, helfe mir aus herzen grunde seliglichen mit innigkeit sprechen: Amen!

Sweet treasury from which all treasures stem; source of all pure springs; guide who leads nobody astray; creator who alone can make something from nothing and nothing from anything; omnipotent animator, upholder and destroyer of things ephemeral, temporal and eternal, whose being in its very self no-one can explore, survey, grasp and understand; greatest good above all goods; most revered and eternal Lord Jesus, receive in Your mercy the spirit, in Your loving kindness the soul of my most beloved wife. Give her peace everlasting, refresh her with the dew of Your grace and take her under the shadow of Your wings. Take her, Lord, into Your perfect bliss, for the least shall have bliss as the greatest. Let her, Lord, from whence she has come, go to dwell in Your realm with the blessed spirits for ever!

Margaret I mourn, the wife of my choice. Merciful Lord, grant that she may see herself in the mirror of Your omnipotent and eternal Godhead, and look and rejoice therein where all the choirs of angels shine.

All creatures that belong under the banner of the eternal standard-bearer, whatsoever they be, help me to say from the depths of my heart in trust and peace: Amen.